Nelson Advanced Modular Science

Thermal Physics

MARK ELLSE • CHRIS HONEYWILL

i

Nelson
Nelson House
Mayfield Road
Walton-on-Thames
Surrey KT12 5PL
UK

First published by Thomas Nelson and Sons Ltd 1998

ISBN 0 17 448262 0
NPN 9 8 7 6 5 4 3
01 00

Picture research by Image Select International Ltd
Printed in China

Publishing team:
Acquisitions: Sonia Clark
Staff editorial: Simon Bell
Freelance editorial: Geoff Amor
Production: Suzanne Howarth
Administration: Sophie Phipps
Design/Typesetting: Hardlines, Charlbury, Oxfordshire

Contents

Acknowledgements

The authors and publishers are grateful for the kind assistance of David Hartley and John Warren for their painstaking work in reading and commenting on the manuscripts. They are also grateful to Dr Alan Cottenden for specialist advice on the Medical Physics Topic and to Dr Jonathan Allday for specialist advice on the Astrophysics Topic.

The authors and publishers are grateful to the following for permission to reproduce copyright photographs:

Science Photo Library: Figures 1.1a (Adrienne Hart-Davis), 1.1c (Adam Hart-Davis), 15.3, A5 (NASA), 18.2 (Peter Menzel), M6 (Scott Camazine), M12 (Matt Meadows), M18 (CNRI), M21 (Simon Fraser/Royal Victoria Infirmary, Newcastle Upon Tyne), A1 (Royal Observatory, Edinburgh), A6 (Space Telescope Science Institute/NASA), A14 (Jeff Hester and Paul Scowen, Arizona State University)

Peter Gould: Figures 1.1b, 4.1, 5.5, 12.3, 16.1, E8
Tony Stone Images: Figure 5.3 (Alastair Black)
Allsport: Figures 6.4 (Vandystadt), 13.2 (Mike Powell)

The authors and publishers are grateful to Edexcel London Examinations for permission to reproduce all the examination questions used in this book.

Preface

This book takes you through the third Module of the Edexcel London Examinations A-level Physics syllabus. It is also suitable for the core content of other A-level schemes. We have divided the book into small chapters, each of which introduces only a few new ideas.

Within the chapters are suggestions for experiments. You may not do or see all the experiments, but you should think about them as you read the text and try to predict what the experiments would show. Most of the experiments are described in a way that you could use yourself as an answer to an examination question that required an experimental description.

Important terms are highlighted in **bold**. There is a list of these terms, under the heading 'Things you need to know' on pages 87–89 of this book.

On pages 71–77 you will find practice questions to try after studying each chapter. There is also a selection of past examination questions.

The chapters are in a possible teaching order, but as far as possible we have tried to make them self-contained so that you can use them in any order, or dip into them for revision.

This book is one of a series of four Module texts for Edexcel London Examinations A-level Physics.

Alongside them is published a set of Experiment Sheets by Adrian Watt which describe in greater detail how to carry out many of the experiments in the texts. There is also a Teacher's Guide, showing how the different publications relate to the examination syllabus and giving guidance on apparatus.

Mark Ellse is Director of Chase Academy, Cannock, Staffordshire, and a Principal Examiner for Edexcel London Examinations.

Chris Honeywill was Deputy Registrar and Head of Physics at The Sixth Form College, Farnborough, Hampshire, and is an Assistant Principal Examiner for Edexcel London Examinations.

Temperature

You can feel a difference in temperature between a very cold and a very hot body, but you need a thermometer to make precise distinctions. There are many different types of thermometer. A common one uses mercury in glass to measure body temperature and for general laboratory measurement. Liquid-crystal thermometers are becoming more common, as are electronic thermometers based on thermocouples (Figure 1.1).

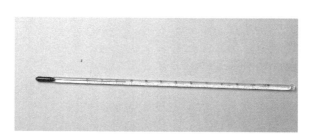

Figure 1.1   Mercury-in-glass thermometers are common in laboratories, but there are others, including alcohol-in-glass, liquid-crystal and thermocouple types

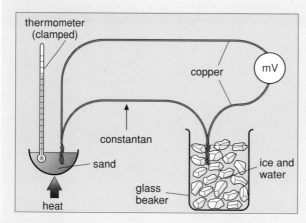

Figure 1.2   One junction of the thermocouple is hot; the other cold

Investigating a thermocouple thermometer

- A thermocouple has two junctions of different metals. Make a thermocouple thermometer as shown in Figure 1.2 by twisting together a piece of constantan wire with two pieces of copper wire. Temporarily put both junctions in the ice and water mix so that they are both at the same temperature. Measure the voltage.
- Keep one junction in the ice and water and put the other junction in the sand. Measure the voltage from the thermocouple for a range of temperatures of the sand. Plot a graph of voltage against temperature.
- Then use the thermocouple to measure the temperatures of the room, your body, a hot drink and a Bunsen flame.

Scales of temperature

To make a thermometer, you need a substance that has a property that changes with temperature. A mercury-in-glass thermometer uses the changing volume of liquid mercury. A thermocouple thermometer uses the changing voltage from a thermocouple. Each of these properties can be used to make a thermometer and to set up a scale of temperature. But before use, a thermometer has first to be marked with a scale, or **calibrated**.

Calibrating a thermometer

- Immerse an uncalibrated thermometer in a mixture of pure ice and water. Stir until the length of the mercury thread remains constant. Then mark the position of the top of the thread with a small elastic band (Figure 1.3).
- Clamp the uncalibrated thermometer in the vapour just above pure boiling water. Again wait until the length of the thread remains constant and again mark the position of the top of the thread.
- Put the thermometer on the bench and allow it to reach the temperature of the laboratory. Make appropriate measurements to find the laboratory temperature.

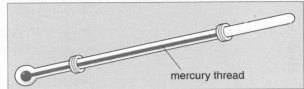

mercury thread

Figure 1.3   Mark the thread position with a small elastic band

Fixed points

To calibrate a thermometer, you need two agreed temperature points. For the Celsius scale these are the **ice point** and the **boiling point** of pure water, called 0°C and 100°C respectively. To calibrate a mercury-in-glass thermometer with a Celsius scale, you find the thread length X_0 and X_{100}, respectively, at these two fixed points.

Then, to measure an unknown temperature θ, measure the thread length X_θ at this temperature.

Assuming that the length of the mercury thread changes in proportion to the temperature, you can see from Figure 1.4 that

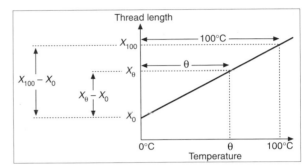

Figure 1.4   The thread length X of a mercury-in-glass thermometer increases with temperature

$$\frac{\theta}{100\,^\circ C} = \frac{X_\theta - X_0}{X_{100} - X_0} \qquad \text{so} \qquad \theta = \frac{X_\theta - X_0}{X_{100} - X_0} \times 100\,^\circ C$$

This formula can be used to calculate a temperature using any property X, but it relies on the property changing in proportion to temperature. Unfortunately, no known property does this precisely.

Accurate temperature measurement requires an agreed standard scale. You can read in Chapters 3 and 8 about the Kelvin scale of temperature, which is the standard used to calibrate all other thermometers.

Thermal equilibrium

If you place a hot object in contact with a cold one, the hot object will give energy to the cold one, and the cold object will receive energy from the hot one. Eventually they will reach the same temperature. They are then in **thermal equilibrium**. This applies when you put a cold thermometer in contact with a hot object. It takes some time for the temperature of the thermometer to rise to that of the hot object. During this process, the temperature of the hot object will fall. Eventually the thermometer and the object will reach the same temperature as each other. Only then will the thermometer indicate the true temperature of the object.

You need to wait for thermal equilibrium between a thermometer and an object before measuring temperature.

You can read more about thermal equilibrium in Chapter 9.

2 **Macroscopic gas properties**

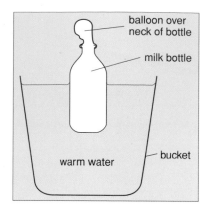

Figure 2.1   What happens as the temperature of the gas increases?

Volume, pressure and temperature

If you raise the temperature of a partially inflated balloon, its volume will increase. If you pump air into a partially inflated balloon, its volume also increases. When the balloon reaches a certain size and the rubber molecules are fully uncoiled, it is very hard to increase the volume further. If you pump more air in, the volume stays roughly the same and the pressure increases until it becomes sufficient to burst the balloon.

Volume, pressure and temperature are the **macroscopic** (large-scale) **properties** of a gas. They are the properties of the gas that you can observe in the laboratory. The pressure, volume and temperature of a gas are interrelated. If you change one, at least one of the others changes. These properties also depend on the amount of gas present. If you want to find out the connection between the macroscopic properties of a gas, you need to experiment with a fixed amount of gas.

A sealed balloon contains a fixed amount of gas. Its volume increases when it is placed in warm water and the temperature rises. But the pressure changes as well. To investigate gas behaviour, as well as keeping the amount of gas constant, you also need to keep one of the other properties constant (either the pressure, the volume or the temperature) and investigate how the remaining two properties depend on each other.

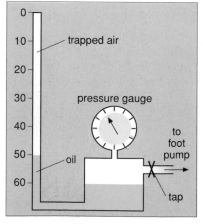

Figure 2.2   The volume decreases when the pressure increases

- Multiply each pressure by its corresponding volume and compare results.
- How would you use the pressure and volume readings to obtain a graph that is a straight line through the origin?

Boyle's law

The volume of a gas decreases as the pressure acting on it increases. The **isothermal** (constant-temperature) curve of Figure 2.3 shows that the volume halves when the pressure doubles, and that it quarters when the pressure increases fourfold. The product (pressure × volume) remains the same:

$$\text{pressure } p \times \text{volume V} = \text{pressure } 2p \times \text{volume } \tfrac{1}{2}\text{V}$$
$$= \text{pressure } 4p \times \text{volume } \tfrac{1}{4}\text{V}$$

Boyle's law states that:

For a fixed mass of gas at constant temperature, the product of the pressure and volume is constant.

Since

$$\text{pressure} \times \text{volume} = \text{constant}$$

we get

$$\text{pressure} = \text{constant/volume}$$

or

$$\text{pressure} \propto 1/\text{volume}$$

Pressure and volume are inversely proportional to each other. A graph of pressure against 1/volume is a straight line through the origin (Figure 2.4).

The dashed line in Figure 2.4 represents the behaviour of the same mass of gas at a higher constant temperature. How would a higher temperature affect the isothermal curve in Figure 2.3?

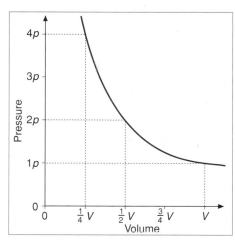

Figure 2.3   Pressure is inversely proportional to volume

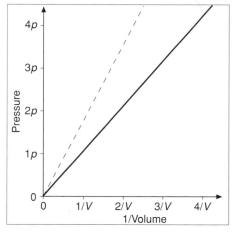

Figure 2.4   Pressure is proportional to 1/volume

Worked example

The cylinder of a pump contains $100\,cm^3$ of air at atmospheric pressure ($100\,000\,Pa$). The piston is pushed in until the volume of the air is reduced by $20\,cm^3$. The air cools back to its original temperature. Calculate the new pressure of the air in the cylinder.

We use the equation
$$\text{pressure} \times \text{volume} = \text{a constant}$$
to find the value of the constant from the initial values for pressure and volume:
$$100\,000\,Pa \times 100\,cm^3 = 1 \times 10^7\,Pa\,cm^3$$
We then use the equation again with the new pressure and new volume:
$$\text{new pressure} \times \text{new volume} = 1 \times 10^7\,Pa\,cm^3$$
We have a new volume of $100\,cm^3 - 20\,cm^3 = 80\,cm^3$ so the new values give
$$\text{new pressure} = (1 \times 10^7\,Pa\,cm^3)/(80\,cm^3) = 125\,000\,Pa$$

The ideal gas equation

Pressure and temperature

- Assemble the apparatus shown in Figure 3.1 and make sure that as much of the flask as possible is submerged in the water bath. Why is it important to use a *short* length of rubber tubing to connect the flask to the pressure gauge?
- Vary the temperature of the water bath by adding ice or heating with the Bunsen burner. Observe the changes to the reading of the pressure gauge. For a range of temperatures, record a series of corresponding readings of the pressure of the gas in the flask and the temperature of the water bath. For each pair of readings, keep the temperature of the water bath steady and allow time for the gas to reach the same temperature.
- Plot a graph of pressure against temperature. Then plot another graph to predict the temperature at which the pressure would become zero.

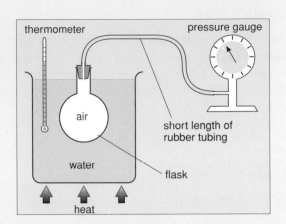

Figure 3.1 *As the temperature increases, the gas pressure increases*

The pressure law

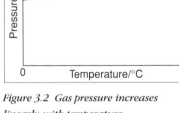

Figure 3.2 *Gas pressure increases linearly with temperature*

A graph of pressure against Celsius temperature is a straight line but it does not pass through the origin (Figure 3.2). The pressure is not zero at 0°C, so pressure is not directly proportional to the Celsius temperature.

If you extrapolate (extend) the graph to lower temperatures as in Figure 3.3, it eventually cuts the temperature axis at approximately –273°C. This is the temperature at which the graph predicts that the pressure would become zero. Experiments with different amounts of gas, and different gases, all predict the same temperature for zero pressure. This temperature is called **absolute zero**, the lowest temperature possible.

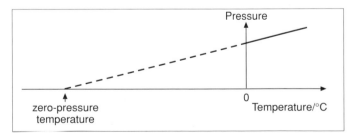

Figure 3.3 *The graph predicts that the pressure would be zero at –273°C*

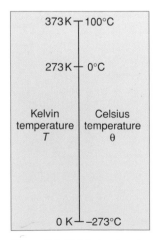

Figure 3.4 *Kelvin temperature = Celsius temperature + 273K*

The Kelvin scale (also called the absolute scale) of temperature *starts* at absolute zero. Figure 3.4 shows the Kelvin scale side by side with the Celsius scale. Zero kelvin (0K) is –273°C. The ice point, 0°C, is 273K. To find the Kelvin temperature, add 273K to the Celsius temperature. It is usual to use the symbol T for Kelvin temperature, and θ for Celsius temperature. So

$$T/K = \theta/°C + 273$$

The graph of pressure against Kelvin temperature is a straight line through the origin. So pressure is proportional to Kelvin temperature. The **pressure law** states that:

> For a fixed mass of gas at constant volume, the pressure is directly proportional to the Kelvin temperature.

Since pressure ∝ Kelvin temperature we can write

$$p \propto T \quad \text{or} \quad p = \text{constant} \times T$$

$$p/T = \text{constant}$$

An ideal gas

All gases will liquefy in the right circumstances. You can liquefy some gases just by raising the pressure, but for other gases you have to reduce the temperature as well. Each gas has a **critical temperature**: below a gas's critical temperature you can liquefy the gas by applying sufficient pressure; above a gas's critical temperature you cannot liquefy the gas at all.

If you compare the behaviour of different gases at modest (around atmospheric) pressures and well above their critical temperatures, you find that they behave similarly and follow closely Boyle's law and the pressure law. It is useful to think of an **ideal gas**, which would obey the gas laws at all temperatures and pressures. An ideal gas like this would have perfect properties to define the Kelvin scale of temperature.

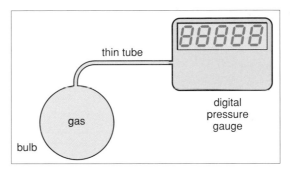

Figure 3.5   Constant-volume gas thermometer. Temperature is defined as being proportional to the pressure of the gas

Figure 3.5 shows a thermometer that uses a constant volume, and constant mass, of gas **(a constant-volume gas thermometer)**. So the gas pressure is proportional to the Kelvin temperature.

The ideal gas equation

Gas pressure is proportional to Kelvin temperature, so pressure divided by Kelvin temperature is constant. Boyle's law states that pressure multiplied by volume is a constant. These two equations may be combined as:

$$pV/T = \text{constant} \quad \text{or} \quad p_1V_1/T_1 = p_2V_2/T_2$$

The value of the constant depends on how much gas is present. For one mole of gas (6.023×10^{23} molecules) this constant is R, the *molar gas constant:*

$$pV/T = R \qquad \text{for one mole of gas}$$

The volume of one mole of any gas at atmospheric pressure ($101\,400\,\text{N}\,\text{m}^{-2}$) and a temperature of $0°\text{C}$ ($273\,\text{K}$) is $0.0224\,\text{m}^3$. From this you can calculate R:

$$R = pV/T = 101\,400\,\text{N}\,\text{m}^{-2} \times 0.0224\,\text{m}^3/273\,\text{K} = 8.3\,\text{N}\,\text{m}\,\text{K}^{-1} = 8.3\,\text{J}\,\text{K}^{-1}$$

A mass m of gas contains m/M moles, where M is the **molar mass** (the mass of a mole). So for a mass m,

$$pV/T = (m/M)R \quad \text{or} \quad pV = (m/M)RT$$

This equation is called the **ideal gas equation**.

Atmospheric pressure

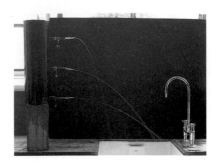

Figure 4.1   Water shoots fastest out of the lowest hole

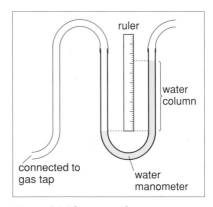

Figure 4.2 The external pressure difference equals the pressure difference caused by the difference in liquid levels

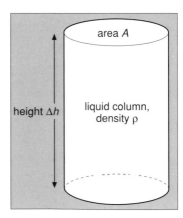

Figure 4.3 Mass of liquid in column = $A\Delta h\rho$

Liquid pressure

Figure 4.1 shows the path of water shooting out of three holes in a can. The water shoots out fastest from the bottom hole, because the water pressure increases at greater depths.

Whether in an irregular container like a teapot, or a more regular one like a U-tube, water normally rises to the same level throughout. If there is a difference in level between two surfaces, like in the U-tube manometer in Figure 4.2, the external pressures on these surfaces must be different. In Figure 4.2, the difference in level is due to the gas supply to which the U-tube is connected. The difference in external pressure is equal to the pressure difference caused by the extra 'column' of liquid on one side.

Figure 4.3 shows a column of liquid on its own. For this column:

$$\text{volume of liquid} \quad = \quad \text{area} \times \text{height} \quad = \quad A\Delta h$$
$$\text{mass of liquid} \quad = \quad \text{volume} \times \text{density} \quad = \quad A\Delta h\rho$$
$$\text{weight of liquid} \quad = \quad mg \quad = \quad A\Delta h\rho g$$

The force exerted on its base by this column of liquid is equal to its weight, $A\Delta h\rho g$.

Pressure is the normal force acting on unit cross-sectional area. The force exerted by a uniform column of liquid equals its weight. So the pressure difference Δp caused by this column of liquid is

$$\Delta p \quad = \quad \text{force/area} \quad = \quad \text{(weight of liquid)/area} \quad = \quad A\Delta h\rho g/A$$

Therefore

$$\Delta p \quad = \quad \Delta h\rho g$$

This formula can be used to calculate fluid pressure difference in any shape of container.

Measuring atmospheric pressure

If you want to measure atmospheric pressure using water as the liquid in the column, you need a manometer over 10 m high. The tube and the bucket in Figure 4.4 act like two sides of a U-tube with one side of the 'U' being much longer than the other. As the vacuum pump removes air from the tube, the pressure inside falls. Atmospheric pressure pushes down on the surface of the water in the bucket and forces some of the water to rise up the empty tube. (Drinking lemonade through a straw works in the same way.)

The water in the long tube reaches a maximum height of about 10 m when the pump has removed all the air in the tube. At this point, the external pressure in the

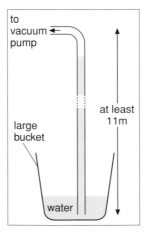

Figure 4.4 Atmospheric pressure can push water up over 10 m

tube is zero and the pressure exerted by the water column is atmospheric. If the top of the tube is now firmly sealed, you can remove the vacuum pump.

Mercury barometer

Mercury is about 14 times denser than water. So you get much smaller height differences for the same pressure differences. A mercury barometer for measuring atmospheric pressure has a sealed central tube containing only a small amount of mercury vapour, evaporated from the mercury surface. Air pressure on the open surface pushes the mercury up the central tube to a height that depends on the slightly variable atmospheric pressure.

Typically, the atmospheric pressure supports a column of mercury 0.76m high:

$$
\begin{aligned}
\text{atmospheric pressure} &= \Delta h \rho_{\text{mercury}} g \\
&= 0.760\,\text{m} \times 13\,600\,\text{kg m}^{-3} \times 9.81\,\text{N kg}^{-1} \\
&= 101\,400\,\text{N m}^{-2} \text{ (or Pa)}
\end{aligned}
$$

Measuring the density of air

- Use a digital balance to measure the mass of a sealed round-bottomed flask filled with air (Figure 4.5). Then evacuate it and measure its mass again. Calculate the mass of air removed.
- Immerse the tube in a bucket of water and slowly let water in. Observe the water rushing into the flask (Figure 4.6).
- Use a measuring cylinder to measure the volume of water that has entered the flask. Assuming that the water has replaced all the air removed by the vacuum pump, calculate the density of air.

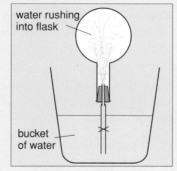

water rushing into flask

bucket of water

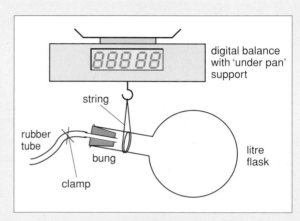

digital balance with 'under pan' support

string

rubber tube

bung

litre flask

clamp

Figure 4.5 Mass of flask includes mass of air inside

Figure 4.6 Atmospheric pressure pushes water into the empty flask

Estimating the height of the atmosphere

Atmospheric pressure is caused by the weight of air above. If this air were all the same density – about 1.3 kg m^{-3} is a typical laboratory figure – you could estimate its height:

$$
\begin{aligned}
\Delta p &= \Delta h \rho g \\
\Delta h &= \Delta p / \rho g \\
&= 101\,400\,\text{Pa}/(1.3\,\text{kg m}^{-3} \times 9.81\,\text{N kg}^{-1}) \\
&= 7.95\,\text{km}
\end{aligned}
$$

Mount Everest is nearly 9km high. It does not stick out of the top of the atmosphere. Our calculation is an underestimate of the height of the atmosphere. The density of air decreases as you get higher. It extends to more than 100km high, and during this its average density is less than 0.1 kg m^{-3}. There is plenty of atmosphere above the summit of Mount Everest!

5 Upthrust and lift

Apparent weight in a fluid

- Suspend a block of aluminium from a forcemeter. Record the weight of the block.
- Slowly lower the block into a large beaker of water until it is fully immersed (Figure 5.1). What happens to the forcemeter's reading as the block is lowered? What happens if the block is lowered further?
- Repeat with the beaker of water on a digital balance. How does the balance reading vary as the block is lowered?

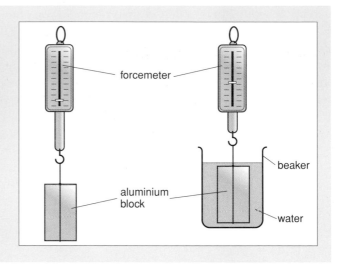

Figure 5.1 The block needs less force from the forcemeter to support it when in water

Upthrust

Fluids exert pressure on immersed objects. The bottom of an immersed object experiences greater fluid pressure than the top because it is at a greater depth. The pressure difference between top and bottom results in an upward force, called **upthrust**, acting on the immersed object. An object appears to weigh less when it is immersed in a fluid. You need less force to lift large boulders in a river than on dry land, for example.

Figure 5.2 shows an upright aluminium cylinder, height Δh and cross-sectional area A, immersed in a fluid of density ρ. The pressure difference Δp between the top and bottom of the cylinder is $\Delta h \rho g$. So

$$\text{upthrust force} = \text{pressure difference} \times \text{area}$$
$$= \Delta h \rho g A = (\Delta h A)\rho g$$
$$= \underline{\text{cylinder}} \text{ volume} \times \underline{\text{fluid}} \text{ density} \times g$$
$$= \text{weight of fluid displaced by the immersed cylinder}$$

The apparent weight of the cylinder when immersed will be less than its actual weight by the above amount. This is summarised in **Archimedes' principle**:

An object that is immersed in a fluid experiences an upthrust equal to the weight of fluid displaced.

If the cylinder is made of wood, its actual weight is less than the upthrust. An additional downward force is needed to keep the cylinder immersed. Removing this force results in the wooden cylinder accelerating upwards. As it passes through the surface, less fluid is displaced. Upthrust is reduced. Equilibrium occurs when the upthrust decreases to equal the weight of the wooden cylinder. The partially immersed cylinder is then floating. An object floats when it displaces its own weight of fluid (Figure 5.3).

liquid surface

depth H

liquid of density ρ

area A

height Δh

aluminium cylinder

Figure 5.2 Upthrust = $\Delta h \rho g A$

We are very familiar with the upthrust that a body experiences in water. But air produces an upthrust too. It is easier to lift an object in air than in a vacuum. If an object is less dense than air, then the upthrust in air will be more than its weight. For instance, a balloon filled with helium will accelerate upwards.

Pressure in a moving fluid

Figure 5.4 shows water flowing through a tube of varying cross-section. The water has to move quicker through the narrow part of the tube. The water gets faster as it enters the constriction and slows down as it leaves. Water rises furthest up the tubes above the wide sections.

As Figure 5.4 shows, water pressure is greatest where the water is moving slowest. The pressure difference between the slow- and fast-moving sections provides the resultant force to accelerate the water.

Aerodynamic lift

If you blow steadily over the top of a sheet of paper held horizontally with one end just below your mouth, the end of the paper moves upwards (Figure 5.5). The pressure of the moving air over the top of a sheet of paper is less than the pressure of the stationary air underneath. The pressure difference creates an upward resultant force on the sheet of paper.

Air moving across the top of an aircraft wing (Figure 5.6) has to travel further than that moving along the bottom. It travels faster across the top, so the air pressure here is lower. The force resulting from this pressure difference produces the **aerodynamic lift** required for an aircraft to fly. Grand Prix racing cars use an inverted wing on the back to create additional down-force and increase the grip for cornering.

Figure 5.3 The weight of this ship is 6.4×10^8 N. It displaces 6.4×10^8 N of sea water

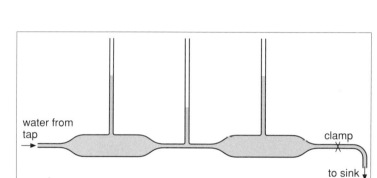

Figure 5.4 The pressure is less where the water moves fastest

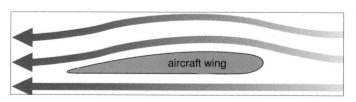

Figure 5.6 Air has to travel faster across the top of an aircraft wing

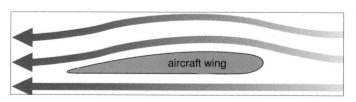

Figure 5.5 The paper rises as you blow over it

Fluid friction

Timing a falling ball

- Fill a tall glass tube with glycerine. Starting from just below the liquid surface, mark off 20 cm sections to the bottom of the tube. Hold a steel ball bearing level with the start of the first section.
- Release the ball bearing and record how long it takes to pass through each section (Figure 6.1). What do the section times tell you about the way in which the ball bearing falls?
- Compare the motion of the falling ball bearing with that of a similar ball bearing released from the same height outside the tube.
- Repeat using ball bearings of different mass.

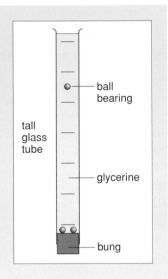

Figure 6.1 Ball bearings fall slowly through glycerine

Terminal speed

The ball bearing takes the same amount of time to pass through each of the lower sections. It accelerates when released but soon reaches a constant speed known as its **terminal speed** (or sometimes **terminal velocity**). At this stage in its motion, the ball bearing is no longer accelerating; it is in *equilibrium*. The resultant of the forces acting on it must be zero.

Drag and viscous forces

At the instant of release there are two forces acting on the ball bearing – its weight and the upthrust from the glycerine. The weight is greater, giving a resultant downward force. Both weight and upthrust remain unchanged throughout the fall. If the ball eventually reaches a constant speed and is in equilibrium, there must be a third force in an upward direction. This is the **drag**. Drag is a force exerted by a fluid which resists the movement of an object through that fluid.

If you try to move your arm through water, you will notice the drag, as you will if you try to move a large balloon through air.

Drag arises for two reasons. It is partly due to **viscous forces** (stickiness) within the fluid. Drag also arises because, as an object moves through a fluid, it has to accelerate the fluid out of its way. At higher speeds the second effect is the more important.

Drag increases with the speed of the object. The faster an object is moving, the greater the drag acting against its motion. The three free-body force diagrams in Figure 6.2 show the ball bearing (a) stationary at the instant of release, (b) accelerating at a reduced rate and (c) moving at its terminal speed.

In all cases:

> **resultant downward force = weight − (upthrust + drag)**

Then we can apply $F = ma$ to this, and rearrange it to give

> **acceleration = [weight − (upthrust + drag)]/mass**

The acceleration is a maximum at the start when drag is momentarily zero. Speed and drag force increase (at a decreasing rate) until

> **weight = upthrust + drag**

At this stage the acceleration is zero and the body moves at its terminal speed. The graphs in Figure 6.3 show how acceleration and velocity vary with time from the instant of release.

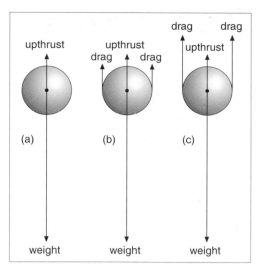

Figure 6.2 When the ball bearing is in equilibrium, its velocity is constant

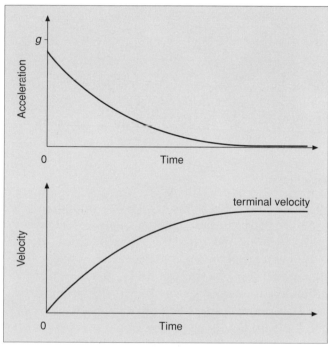

Figure 6.3 As the velocity increases, the acceleration decreases

Figure 6.4 Most of the time skydivers are in equilibrium – their velocity is constant

Falling through air

If you drop a ball bearing through air rather than through glycerine, it needs to travel much further to reach a terminal speed. And the terminal speed would be much higher. Air is less viscous and less dense than glycerine. It produces less drag for the same speed and less upthrust.

Skydivers in 'free-fall' reach terminal speeds that can exceed 100 mph (Figure 6.4). Since the atmosphere is less dense at higher altitude, they have a greater terminal speed at a height of 3000 m than they do at 1000 m.

A raindrop falling from a cloud at a height of 1000 m solely under the influence of gravity would hit the ground at a speed of $140\,\mathrm{m\,s^{-1}}$, whereas their actual speed is usually much less than $10\,\mathrm{m\,s^{-1}}$. If it were not for the effect of air drag forces, we would have to wear steel helmets whenever it was raining!

7 Modelling the behaviour of a gas

Observing smoke

- Use the lamp to illuminate the glass tube (Figure 7.1): the glass rod acts as a lens and focuses light from the lamp inside the tube.
- Hold the unlit end of a burning straw above the tube. Close the container and trap some smoke inside.
- Observe the smoke through a microscope. Smoke particles appear as very small bright dots. They reflect light from the lamp into the microscope. What are the smoke particles doing? What makes them move in this way?

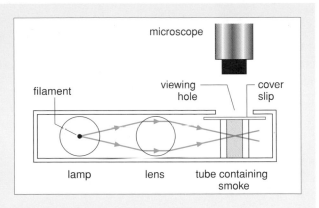

Figure 7.1 The tube contains smoke

Brownian motion

Smoke consists of small particles suspended in the air. You can see the particles under a microscope. They dance about randomly, moving first one way and then immediately another. The motion of the smoke particles that you can see in the school laboratory experiment above is due to turbulence (disturbance) of the air. But even if you take special care to make sure that the air is still, you can still see random motion of the smoke particles. A botanist, Robert Brown, first saw similar movement when he observed pollen grains in water and gave his name to this random, zigzag motion.

Brownian motion of the smoke particles provides evidence that air consists of particles moving randomly at high speeds. The visible smoke particles are being knocked about by air molecules hitting them. Smoke particles are small and light. The small size means that there will nearly always be more air molecules hitting one side than another at any instant (Figure 7.2). So there will be a resultant force pushing the particle in different directions from moment to moment. The very low mass means that the constantly changing resultant force is sufficient to move the particle, as seen by the microscope.

Smoke particles are small but air molecules are very much smaller. Air molecules must be moving at very high speeds to have sufficient momentum to cause the heavier smoke particles to move with Brownian motion.

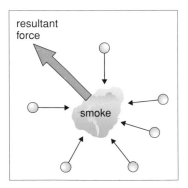

Figure 7.2 At a given instant, the forces on the smoke particle are unbalanced

Modelling a gas

- In the model of a gas shown in Figure 7.3, small ball bearings represent air molecules. Unlike air molecules, their collisions are not elastic, so the motor is needed to keep them moving.
- Increase the speed of the motor to make the molecules move faster. What happens to the volume, indicated by the height of the cardboard disc?
- Add mass to the cardboard disc. What effect does this have on the volume?
- Then remove the cardboard disc. Observe the distribution of the ball bearings.
- Place a small polystyrene sphere (representing a smoke particle) in with the ball bearings. Switch on the motor and observe the Brownian motion of the sphere.

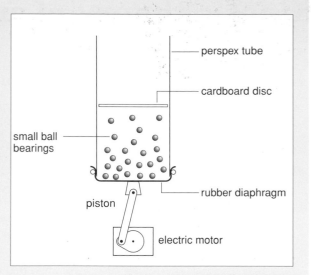

Figure 7.3 The ball bearings represent gas molecules

Gas laws and the mechanical model

The collisions of the ball bearings with the cardboard disc exert a force on it. In a similar way, the molecules of a gas exert a force on the walls of their container as they collide with it. Faster movement of the ball bearings corresponds to an increase in temperature.

If you keep the volume occupied by the ball bearings constant and increase their speed, the ball bearings hit the container walls harder and more frequently, producing an increased pressure. This corresponds to the pressure law.

If the cardboard disc is free to rise, an increase in the speed of the ball bearings will produce an increase in volume. The pressure exerted by the molecules remains the same. They hit the sides of the container harder, but less often.

Adding weight to the cardboard disc increases the pressure and reduces the volume. This increases the packing density of its molecules (Figure 7.4). The number of collisions made with the walls increases and produces a greater pressure. This corresponds to Boyle's law.

The ball bearings in our model stop moving when the motor is turned off. They soon lose their kinetic energy – their collisions are *inelastic*. The average kinetic energy of gas molecules in a constant-temperature enclosure remains the same. The molecules do not lose their kinetic energy – their collisions are *elastic*.

The atmosphere is denser near the Earth; its molecules are further apart at greater heights. Similarly the ball bearings are more densely packed at the bottom of the cylinder, where they exert a greater pressure, and thin out with height.

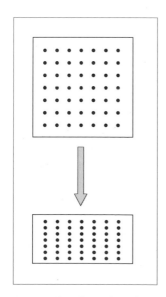

Figure 7.4 Halving the volume doubles the packing density

8 | Kinetic theory of an ideal gas

Assumptions about gas molecules

Experimental observation led physicists to make some assumptions about gases, which led to a theoretical model of a gas.

- From Brownian motion they assumed that gases consist of identical molecules in continuous random motion.
- Molecules never come to a stop and settle at the bottom of the container, so they assumed that molecular collisions are on average elastic.
- You can compress a gas a lot, so they assumed that the volume of the molecules is negligible compared with the volume of the container.
- Therefore, the molecules must be a relatively long way apart, so they assumed that there are no forces on the molecules except during collisions.

A theoretical model of a gas

Figure 8.1 shows a box whose sides are of length x, y and z. A single gas molecule, mass m, is bouncing between the shaded face and its opposite one with speed u. Taking rightwards as positive, the momentum of the molecule *after* colliding with the left-hand face is $+mu$; *before* the collision it was $-mu$ (Figure 8.2). So

$$\text{change of momentum} = \text{final momentum} - \text{initial momentum}$$
$$= +mu - (-mu) = 2mu$$

The molecule travels a distance $2x$ between collisions with the *shaded* face:

$$\text{time between collisions} = \text{distance/speed} = 2x/u$$

Force exerted on shaded wall by molecule = rate of change of momentum:

$$\text{force} = (\text{change of momentum})/\text{time} = 2mu/(2x/u) = mu^2/x$$

We can now find the pressure exerted by the single molecule on the shaded face:

$$\text{pressure} = \text{force/area} = (mu^2/x)/yz = mu^2/xyz$$

But xyz = volume V of the box, so for a single molecule

$$\text{pressure} = mu^2/V$$

In a real box of gas, there are N molecules moving randomly. You can assume that, on average, only a third of these are colliding with the shaded face and its opposite, and a third on each of the other pairs of faces. The molecules do not all move at the same speed u, but have a range of speeds, and their average or mean square speed is written as $\langle c^2 \rangle$. Therefore

$$\text{total pressure } p = \tfrac{1}{3}Nm\langle c^2 \rangle/V \quad \text{so} \quad pV = \tfrac{1}{3}Nm\langle c^2 \rangle$$

Root mean square speed

The product $N \times m$ is the total mass of gas in the box. Nm/V gives the density ρ. So the previous equation can be written

$$p = \tfrac{1}{3}\rho\langle c^2 \rangle$$

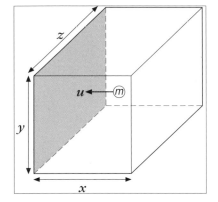

Figure 8.1 A single gas molecule, mass m, is bouncing between the shaded face and its opposite with speed u

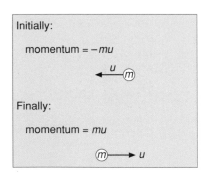

Initially:

momentum = $-mu$

Finally:

momentum = mu

Figure 8.2 Change of momentum = mu − (−mu) = 2mu

Atmospheric pressure is about 100 kPa and the density of air is about $1 \, kg \, m^{-3}$. Using these values we can find the mean square speed of air molecules:

$$\langle c^2 \rangle = 3p/\rho = 3 \times 100\,000 \, \text{Pa}/1 \, kg \, m^{-3} = 300\,000 \, m^2 \, s^{-2}$$

The **root mean square (r.m.s.) speed** is the square root of the mean square speed, where the mean square speed is the sum of the squares of the molecular speeds divided by the total number of molecules. For the air molecules:

$$\text{r.m.s. speed} = \sqrt{(300\,000 \, m^2 \, s^{-2})} = 550 \, m \, s^{-1}$$

It is not surprising that the speed of sound, about $340 \, m \, s^{-1}$, is comparable with this, since the molecules convey the sound waves.

Molecular speed and temperature

For one mole of gas, the equation $pV = \frac{1}{3}Nm\langle c^2 \rangle$ becomes

$$pV = \frac{1}{3} N_A m \langle c^2 \rangle$$

where N_A is the *Avogadro constant*, the number of molecules in one mole. So

$$pV = \frac{2}{3} N_A \times \frac{1}{2} m \langle c^2 \rangle$$

where $\frac{1}{2} m \langle c^2 \rangle$ is the mean kinetic energy of a single molecule. This equation has to agree with the ideal gas equation for one mole of gas, $pV = RT$. So

$$\frac{2}{3} N_A \times \frac{1}{2} m \langle c^2 \rangle = RT \quad \text{or} \quad \frac{1}{2} m \langle c^2 \rangle = \frac{3}{2} (R/N_A)T$$

R/N_A, the molar gas constant divided by the Avogadro constant, is the gas constant per molecule, known as the *Boltzmann constant k*, where

$$k = R/N_A = (8.3 \, J \, K^{-1} \, mol^{-1})/(6.02 \times 10^{23} \, mol^{-1}) = 1.38 \times 10^{-23} \, J \, K^{-1}$$

$$\text{So} \quad \frac{1}{2} m \langle c^2 \rangle = \frac{3}{2} kT$$

This equation states that the average molecular kinetic energy is proportional to the Kelvin temperature. This equation is now used to define temperature as that quantity which is proportional to the molecular kinetic energy of an ideal gas.

Distribution of molecular speeds

Although the air molecules around you have an r.m.s. speed of $550 \, m \, s^{-1}$, at a given instant some of them will be almost stationary while others will be moving at over three times this value.

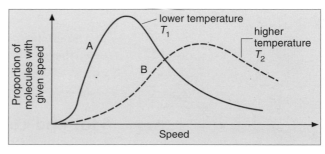

Figure 8.3 shows the distribution of speeds in the molecules of a gas. Graph A shows the distribution for a lower temperature, T_1. Graph B shows the distribution for the same amount of gas at a higher temperature, T_2.

The area under the curve is proportional to the number of molecules. So both graphs A and B have the same area.

Figure 8.3 At higher temperatures the mean speed of the molecules increases, although the proportion of the molecules in a given range around this particular speed is less

Internal energy

You studied internal energy in Chapter 19 of *Mechanics and Electricity*. In the previous two chapters of this book you have learned about the way that the molecules inside a gas behave. You can put these two pieces of physics together to understand what internal energy is.

The molecules of a gas are moving around. Molecules with more than one atom can also spin and vibrate. All these movements can store kinetic energy.

If you could look inside a gas, you might occasionally see two molecules heading directly towards each other, slowing down, stopping, and then springing away from each other as shown in Figure 9.1.

What has happened to the kinetic energy of those molecules? As the molecules get close, there are repulsive forces between them. At the point where both molecules are stationary, all their kinetic energy has been converted into potential energy stored by doing work against the repulsive forces between the molecules.

When the molecules in a gas are colliding, they are working against these repulsive forces and there is a continual interchange between kinetic and potential energy.

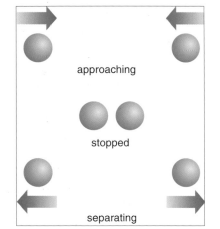

Figure 9.1 When the molecules are stationary, all the energy is potential

The random kinetic and potential energy inside a gas is its **internal energy**. If you raise the temperature of the gas, the molecules move faster and approach closer when they collide; they have more random kinetic and potential energy. So raising the temperature of a body raises its internal energy.

The internal energy of other bodies is also the sum of the molecular kinetic and potential energies. In a solid, the molecules cannot move around, but they are vibrating, constantly swapping kinetic energy for potential energy and vice versa.

In a liquid the motion of the molecules is somewhere in between the behaviour of a solid and a gas, but, just the same, the kinetic and potential energy of its molecules make up the internal energy of the liquid.

Hot and cold bodies

The molecules of a body act as tiny stores of kinetic and potential energy. Each molecule has a number of independent ways of moving – from side to side, up and down, rotating, vibrating and so on (Figure 9.2). These are called **degrees of freedom**. Each degree of freedom can store energy, and together the energy of these degrees of freedom make up the internal energy of the body.

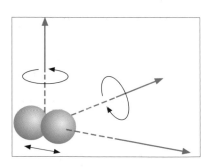

Figure 9.2 The molecule can store energy by moving in three directions, by rotating and by vibrating

In a hot body, each degree of freedom has, on average, a large amount of energy. In a cold body, each degree of freedom has, on average, a small amount of energy.

The energy in a body is spread randomly amongst the degrees of freedom. Also, the distribution of the energy changes as it shuffles about randomly from one degree of freedom to another.

Figure 9.3 represents the degrees of freedom of two bodies as a number of boxes. The dots each represent a unit of energy. In the hot body B, each degree of freedom has, on average, 2 units of energy. But you can see that at one instant any one degree of freedom might have 0, 1, 2, 3 units of energy, or even more. Only on average will it have 2 units. The cold body A has an average of 1 unit of energy per degree of freedom.

Heating

If you put a hot body (large amount of energy per degree of freedom) in thermal contact with a cold body (small amount of energy per degree of freedom), then the energy shuffles randomly between the two bodies. Sometimes energy goes from the hot body to the cold body; and sometimes energy goes from the cold body to the hot body. But on average, since there is more energy per degree of freedom in the hot body, energy goes from the hot body to the cold body.

Random shuffling of quanta like this eventually results in the energy evening out, so that both bodies have the same amount of energy per degree of freedom – they both have the same temperature. Figure 9.4 shows the bodies of Figure 9.3 after they have been in contact for a while. On average both sides have 1.5 units of energy per degree of freedom.

Thermal equilibrium

When the two bodies have reached the same temperature, energy shuffling still takes place. But now, since both bodies have the same amount of energy per degree of freedom, on average there is no net flow of energy from one to the other. Energy flows from A to B and from B to A at the same rate. The two bodies are in thermal equilibrium with no net energy flow and, as you read in Chapter 1, their temperatures are the same.

Heat transfer

The flow of internal energy like this, caused by a temperature difference, is called **heat** or **heat transfer**.

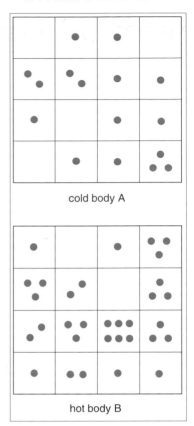

cold body A

hot body B

Figure 9.3 The hot body has more energy per degree of freedom

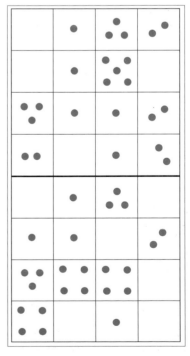

Figure 9.4 When you put hot and cold bodies into contact, the distribution of energy evens out

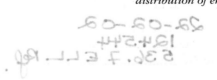

10 Conduction, convection and radiation

Good and bad conductors

- In turn, hold copper, iron and glass rods by one end while the other end is in a Bunsen flame (Figure 10.1).
- Which material conducts best?

Good and bad conductors

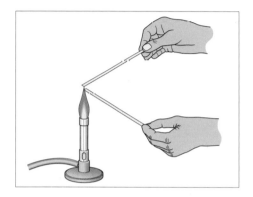

Figure 10.1 You can feel which rod conducts better

Thermal conduction is the flow of internal energy through a material that does not move. Some materials are good thermal conductors. Diamond is a good conductor: internal energy can move rapidly through the regularly and rigidly fastened atoms. Metals are good conductors because electrons inside them can move freely and take energy with them. Glass, with its irregular structure, less-rigid bonds and absence of free electrons, is a poor conductor.

Liquids are poorer conductors. Their molecules are not fastened so firmly to their neighbours, so they cannot transfer energy so easily.

The molecules in a gas are in contact only during collisions. They can only exchange energy by travelling. So gases are poor conductors.

Convection and radiation

- Shine light from a projector through the space above a heater. Observe the movement of the air above the heater (Figure 10.2).
- Hold your hand near a radiant heater. Then put a screen in the way (Figure 10.3). Experiment with removing and replacing the screen to see how quickly energy travels from the heater.

Convection

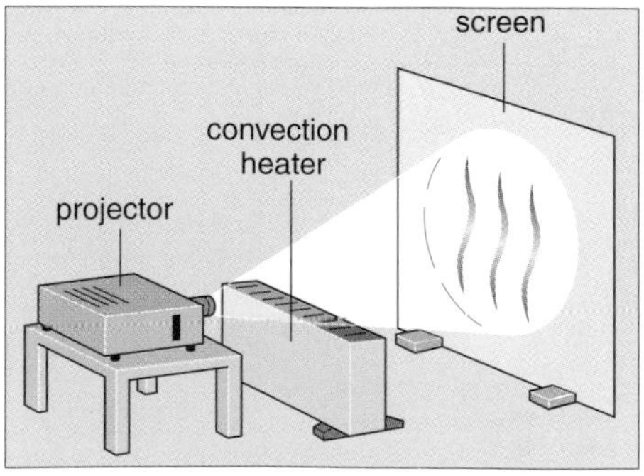

Figure 10.2 The pattern on the screen shows the movement of the air

Convection takes place when a medium moves and takes internal energy with it. Natural convection takes place when the temperature of a gas or a liquid is uneven. Where the fluid is hotter, it is less dense. So the upthrust from the surrounding colder fluid is greater than the weight of the warm fluid. There is then a net upward force which pushes the warm fluid up.

Sometimes something like the wind, a pump or a fan pushes a fluid around. Forced convection can then take place as the moving fluid conveys internal energy with it. On a windy day you feel colder because the wind takes away the warm layer of air around you faster than natural convection would take it. A pump in a nuclear reactor pushes cooling fluid quickly round the core to take energy from the core to the boiler.

Radiation

You studied electromagnetic radiation in *Matter and Waves*. Electromagnetic radiation is emitted from bodies at all temperatures, but the intensity is greater with increasing temperature. The electromagnetic quanta transfer energy at the speed of light. When another body absorbs them, they raise its internal energy.

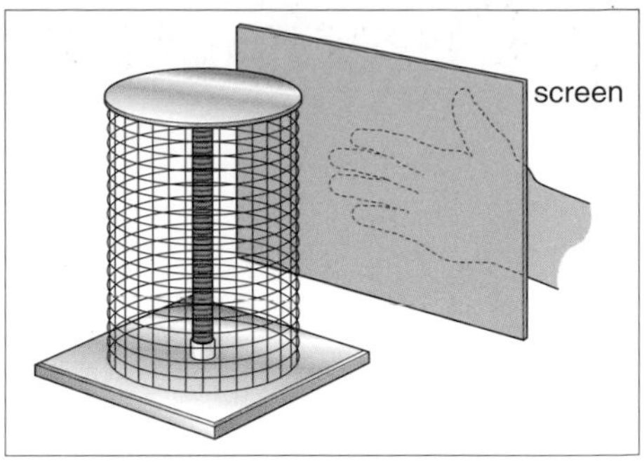

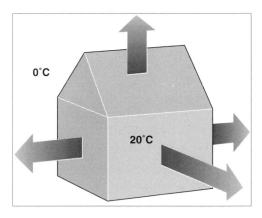

Figure 10.3 Remove the screen and notice how quickly your hand gets hot

Evaporation

Random shuffling of energy results in molecules occasionally having much more energy than the average. Sometimes a molecule near the surface of a liquid, or even a solid, will have sufficient energy to break free of the rest. This is **evaporation**. During evaporation, energy is used to break the bonds holding molecules together. The average energy of the remaining molecules is therefore less – they are colder. When you are hot, you sweat, taking advantage of this cooling by evaporation to lose internal energy and bring your temperature down.

Keeping warm

In the British climate, for much of the year our surroundings are at a colder temperature than we, personally, would like to be. Our body temperature is about 37 °C and, when clothed, we are comfortable in surroundings that are about 20 °C. But the outdoor temperatures are usually less than that. So, for much of the year, we keep our homes at higher temperatures than the outside.

When the insides of our houses are hotter than the outsides, internal energy flows outwards through the walls (Figure 10.4). If we want to keep the insides warm, we need continuously to make up for this loss. This is the function of home heating.

Figure 10.4 When the outside is colder than the inside of your house, energy leaks out

Steady state

Though inside and outside temperatures change, there are some parts of the day when you can regard the inside temperature as constant, perhaps at 20 °C, and the outside temperature as constant, perhaps at 10 °C. If these temperatures remain steady for some time, the temperature of the structure of the building becomes steady. The temperatures across the bricks have become constant, with, perhaps, a temperature in the middle of 15 °C, half-way between the inside and outside temperatures. This situation is known as **steady state**. There is steady flow of internal energy from the inside of the house to the outside, but all temperatures are remaining constant.

Steady state is quite different from thermal equilibrium. In thermal equilibrium, all the temperatures are the same. There is no net flow of internal energy at all. In steady state, the temperatures are constant but different, and there are steady flows of internal energy.

Thermal conductivity

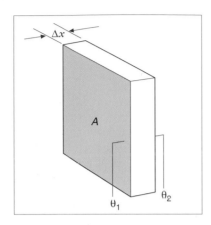

Figure 11.1 *Internal energy flows through the shaded area*

Table 11.1 *Some thermal conductivities*

Material	Thermal conductivity /W m^{-1} K^{-1}
copper	390
diamond	165
iron	75
brick	~1
polythene	0.3
insulating block	0.2

Table 11.2 *Some U-values*

Construction	U-value /W m^{-2} K^{-1}
220 mm brick	2.1
brick cavity wall	1.6
brick cavity wall, filled with foam	0.6
insulating block wall, filled with foam	0.4
single-glazed window	4.3
double-glazed window	2.5
concrete floor, with carpet	0.5
tiled roof, no insulation	1.8
tiled roof, with 100 mm glass wool	0.3

Maintaining the steady state

On a cold day, energy from inside a warm house continually leaks out through the walls, windows, floor and roof. If the energy is not replaced, the house gradually cools down. We buy gas, electricity or other fuels to make up for these losses. It is useful to make a mathematical model of the energy flow through the wall so that we can identify the losses and work out how to reduce them.

Thermal conductivity

Figure 11.1 shows a sample of material of area A and thickness Δx. The temperatures on either side are θ_1 and θ_2. If θ_1 is greater than θ_2, energy flows from θ_1 to θ_2. The temperature difference $\theta_1 - \theta_2$ is written as $\Delta\theta$; the temperature difference $\Delta\theta$ is what drives internal energy through the sample.

The rate of flow of energy, the flow of energy per second, is the power flow through the walls. The power depends on the size of the sample and the temperature difference. It also depends on the material's ability to conduct – its **thermal conductivity** k. We find that

$$\text{power} = \frac{\text{thermal conductivity} \times \text{area} \times \text{temperature difference}}{\text{thickness}}$$

$$P = kA\Delta\theta/\Delta x$$

Rearranging the above equation gives

$$k = P\Delta x/A\Delta\theta$$

The units of k are $(\text{W m})/(\text{m}^2\text{K}) = \text{W}/(\text{m K}) = \text{W m}^{-1}\text{ K}^{-1}$.

The thermal conductivity is high for a good conductor and low for a bad conductor. Table 11.1 shows values for a range of materials.

Now consider a brick wall 0.225 m thick of thermal conductivity 1.2 W m^{-1}K^{-1}. The power flow P through a wall 3 m high and 4 m wide, on a day when the inside temperature is 20 °C and the outside 2 °C, would be:

$$P = kA\Delta\theta/\Delta x$$

$$= 1.2\,\text{W m}^{-1}\text{K}^{-1} \times 3\,\text{m} \times 4\,\text{m} \times (20 - 2)\,\text{K}/0.225\,\text{m} = 1152\,\text{W}$$

If you replace the brick with insulating block of the same thickness, the losses decrease to 192 W.

U-values

Walls of buildings have a complicated construction, often with several layers of different types of materials. To calculate the losses through them, engineers use standard tables of **U-values** (Table 11.2).

U-values are equivalent to the effective thermal conductivity divided by the thickness for a particular wall, floor or roof construction:

$$U\text{-value} = U = (\text{effective thermal conductivity})/\text{thickness} = k/\Delta x$$

The equation for power given opposite can be written as

$$P = kA\Delta\theta/\Delta x = (k/\Delta x)A\Delta\theta = UA\Delta\theta$$

Table 11.2 gives U-values for a range of building constructions.

Worked example

Calculate the total power loss from the bungalow in Figure 11.2 when the inside temperature is 21°C and the outside is 0°C. The bungalow has a tiled roof with no insulation, a concrete floor with carpet, solid brick walls and single-glazed windows.

For roof, $\quad P = UA\Delta\theta = 1.8\,\mathrm{W\,m^{-2}\,K^{-1}} \times 80\,\mathrm{m^2} \times 21\,\mathrm{K} = 3024\,\mathrm{W}$

For floor, $\quad P = UA\Delta\theta = 0.5\,\mathrm{W\,m^{-2}\,K^{-1}} \times 80\,\mathrm{m^2} \times 21\,\mathrm{K} = 840\,\mathrm{W}$

For walls, $\quad P = UA\Delta\theta = 2.1\,\mathrm{W\,m^{-2}\,K^{-1}} \times 90\,\mathrm{m^2} \times 21\,\mathrm{K} = 3969\,\mathrm{W}$

For windows, $\quad P = UA\Delta\theta = 4.3\,\mathrm{W\,m^{-2}\,K^{-1}} \times 18\,\mathrm{m^2} \times 21\,\mathrm{K} = 1625\,\mathrm{W}$

Total loss $\hspace{9cm} = 9458\,\mathrm{W}$

A similar bungalow has a roof insulated with 100 mm glass wool, the walls made from insulating block filled with foam, and double-glazed windows. The losses would be

roof 504 W, floor 840 W, walls 756 W, windows 945 W, total 3045 W

Thermal insulation

The total power loss of 9458 W from the first bungalow is a loss of about 230 kWh in a day – nearly £10 per day if heating by gas. Of course, the cost for heating for a whole year would not be 365 times as much as this, because the average outside temperature is higher than 0°C. But the second bungalow, with losses of about a third of the first bungalow, would be much cheaper to keep warm.

In the better-insulated bungalow losses through the walls are reduced from 3969 W to 756 W, through the roof from 3024 W to 504 W, and through the windows from 1625 W to 945 W. Although replacing the solid walls would save most, it is obviously very difficult to do in practical terms. You can fill cavity walls with foam or mineral wool, but there are major difficulties insulating solid walls and controlling moisture in them.

Roof insulation saves almost as much and is quite cheap and easy to do by putting a layer of glass wool in the loft. This works by trapping air, just like lagging a pipe or a beaker.

Double glazing is popular but does not actually save a lot. But it has other benefits by reducing noise and preventing draughts.

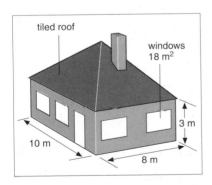

Figure 11.2 The floor and effective roof areas of the bungalow are 80 m²; the walls have an area of 90 m² plus windows with an area of 18 m²

12 Specific heat capacity

Heating water

- Put 100g of water in a lagged plastic beaker with a heater and a thermometer (Figure 12.1). Measure the starting temperature. Supply 1000J of energy to the water, measured with a joulemeter. Stir the water and measure the final temperature.
- Add energy in further 1000J steps until the temperature has risen by about 15K. Plot a graph of temperature rise against energy supplied.
- Repeat the experiment with 200g of water. What differences do you observe?

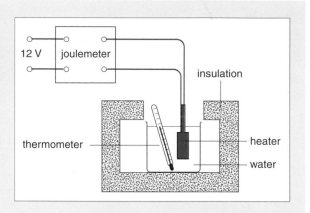

Figure 12.1 The joulemeter measures the energy supplied

Heat capacity

If you raise the temperature of an object, you increase the kinetic energy of its molecules – you increase its internal energy. So you need to supply energy. The energy needed to raise the temperature of an object is proportional to the increase in temperature. For an increase of one kelvin (1 K), the energy needed is called the **heat capacity** H of that object. So

$$\text{energy needed} = \text{heat capacity} \times \text{temperature rise}$$
$$\text{energy} = H\Delta T$$

so that

$$H = \text{energy}/\Delta T$$

The units of H are J K^{-1}.

The heat capacity of a particular object depends on its mass, and on the substances of which it is made. In general, the heat capacities of different objects are all different, so heat capacities are of limited use.

Table 12.1 *Some specific heat capacities*

Material	Specific heat capacity / J kg⁻¹ K⁻¹
lead	130
copper	380
iron	450
aluminium	880
concrete block	920
water	4200

Specific heat capacity

It is much more useful to know the energy needed to raise the temperature of a pure substance. The amount of energy required is proportional to the mass of the substance and the temperature rise:

$$\text{energy} \propto \text{mass} \times \text{temperature rise}$$

The constant of proportionality depends on the substance you are heating. It is called the **specific heat capacity** c (Table 12.1). So

$$\text{energy} = \text{mass} \times \text{specific heat capacity} \times \text{temperature rise}$$
$$\text{energy} = mc\Delta T$$

so that $\quad c = \text{energy}/m\Delta T$

The units of specific heat capacity are $\text{J/(kg K)} = \text{J kg}^{-1}\text{K}^{-1}$.

Measuring the specific heat capacity of aluminium

- Take an aluminium block drilled to take a heater and thermometer and measure its mass. Lag the block and insert the heater and thermometer (Figure 12.2). Measure the initial temperature.
- Turn the heater on for 2 min and measure the voltage and current. Continue to measure the temperature after you turn the heater off and record the highest temperature reached.
- Calculate the
  energy supplied = voltage × current × time.
- Divide the energy by the mass and the temperature rise to calculate the specific heat capacity.

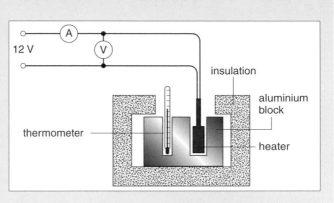

Figure 12.2 Measure voltage, current and time to calculate the energy supplied

Specific heat capacity and the mass of molecules

A copper atom is much more massive than an aluminium atom. This means that a kilogram of copper has many fewer atoms than a kilogram of aluminium. Each atom of copper or aluminium needs about the same energy for each 1 K rise in temperature. It is easier to raise the temperature of 1 kg of copper through 1 K than to raise the temperature of 1 kg of aluminium by the same amount. The specific heat capacity of copper is about $380\,\mathrm{J\,kg^{-1}K^{-1}}$; that of aluminium is about $880\,\mathrm{J\,kg^{-1}K^{-1}}$. You can see from Table 12.1 that materials with massive molecules have low specific heat capacities.

Electric storage heaters store internal energy. They receive energy from the electricity supply during the night (when it is cheaper!) and give it out during the day. Storage heaters are heavy: they need a large mass to store a large amount of internal energy. But their designers want to minimise their mass. For a given temperature rise, a substance with a high specific heat capacity can store more energy per kilogram. So storage heaters use materials of high specific heat capacity – generally concrete blocks. Though the blocks have only a quarter of the specific heat capacity of water, they can be raised through a much higher temperature, and therefore store more energy per kilogram.

Worked example

The specific heat capacity of water is $4200\,\mathrm{J\,kg^{-1}K^{-1}}$. Calculate the energy needed to raise a kettle-full of water, volume 1.4 litres, from tap temperature, 10°C, to boiling point.

The density of water is $1.0\,\mathrm{kg\,l^{-1}}$ and so the mass of 1.4 litres of water is 1.4 kg. To find the energy needed, we use

energy = mass × specific heat capacity × temperature rise

= $1.4\,\mathrm{kg} \times 4200\,\mathrm{J\,kg^{-1}K^{-1}} \times (100 - 10)\,\mathrm{K} = 0.53\,\mathrm{MJ}$

Energy costs about 2p per megajoule from the electricity supply. So the cost of heating this kettle-full of water is about 1.06p.

Specific latent heat

Measuring the energy required to boil away water

- Put a measuring cylinder on a top pan balance and surround the cylinder with lagging. Support a heater as shown in Figure 13.1. Fill the measuring cylinder with boiling water and turn on the power supply. Wait until the water comes back to the boil.
- Measure the voltage and current supplied to the heater. Then time how long it takes to boil away 5 g of water.
- Calculate the energy required to boil away 1 kg of water.

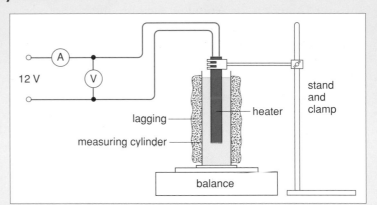

Figure 13.1 The heater boils away the water

Specific latent heat

You need energy to turn a liquid into a vapour. The energy is used to tear the molecules apart, greatly increasing their potential energy. The energy required to turn 1 kg of a particular liquid to vapour at the same temperature is called its **specific latent heat of vaporisation** L.

To vaporise a given mass of a substance:

energy = mass × specific latent heat of vaporisation

energy = mL

You also need energy to turn a solid into a liquid. Again, the energy is used to increase the potential energy of the molecules, releasing the molecules from their fixed positions, but not freeing them from their neighbours completely. The energy required to turn 1 kg of a particular solid to liquid at the same temperature is called its **specific latent heat of fusion** L.

To melt a given mass of a substance:

energy = mass × specific latent heat of fusion

energy = mL

When we get hot, we sweat, as Figure 13.2 shows. The sweat needs energy, its latent heat of vaporisation, to evaporate. It takes that from the body and cools the body down.

Figure 13.2 We sweat to keep our temperature low

Measuring the specific latent heat of fusion of water

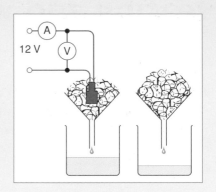

* Set up two funnels filled with crushed ice as shown in Figure 13.3. Put a heater (not yet turned on) in one of the funnels and leave them both for a minute so the heater reaches the temperature of the ice.
* Turn on the heater and record the voltage and current supplied. Catch the water melted from each funnel in a time of 2 min and measure its mass. Subtract the mass of water collected from the funnel without the heater from that collected from the funnel with the heater, to find the extra mass of ice melted by the heater.
* Why is some ice melted in the funnel without the heater? Why do you subtract this from the mass melted in the other funnel?
* Calculate the energy supplied to the heater and divide it by the mass of ice melted by the heater to find the specific latent heat of fusion of ice (water) in J kg^{-1}.

Figure 13.3 More ice melts in the side with the heater

Worked example

A kettle has an element with a power of 2.2 kW. When full of water, it remains turned on for 2 min after the water reaches boiling point. The specific latent heat of vaporisation of water is 2.3 MJ kg^{-1}. Calculate the mass of water boiled off.

Energy supplied is given by

$$\text{energy} = \text{power} \times \text{time} = 2200\,\text{W} \times 120\,\text{s} = 264\,000\,\text{J} = 0.264\,\text{MJ}$$

Mass of water boiled off is found from

$$\text{energy} = \text{mass vaporised} \times \text{specific latent heat of vaporisation}$$

so

$$\text{mass vaporised} = \text{energy}/(\text{specific latent heat of vaporisation})$$

$$= 0.264\,\text{MJ}/(2.3\,\text{MJ kg}^{-1}) = 0.115\,\text{kg} = 115\,\text{g}$$

Of course, not all of the 2.2 kW being supplied is being used to boil the water. Some of it is being lost to the surroundings by conduction, convection and radiation. So, in practice, the amount boiled off in 2 min will be less than 115 g.

Enthalpy

As stated above, you increase the potential energy of the molecules when you change a solid to a liquid, or a liquid to its vapour. You therefore increase the internal energy of the substance. If the surrounding pressure is constant during these changes of state, the substance will change volume – usually expanding when going from solid to liquid or from liquid to vapour. As you can read in more detail in the next chapter, this means that the substance does work on its surroundings.

Therefore, the energy supplied for a change of state is partly used to increase the internal energy of the substance involved and partly to work on the surroundings. This energy supplied is called the *enthalpy*. For this reason, the specific latent heat is sometimes called the **specific enthalpy**.

So for a change of state from liquid to gas you could write:

enthalpy supplied = mass × specific enthalpy of vaporisation

Heating and working

Figure 14.1 Beat the lead block and observe the change in temperature

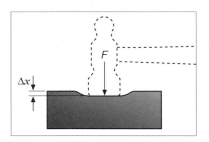

Figure 14.2 Work done = F∆x

Mechanical working

When you squash a lead block, you apply a force to it which moves in the direction of the force. You are doing work on the block. This is **mechanical working**. The lead is hard to distort; you need large forces to compress it a small distance. You can calculate the work done by multiplying the average force by the distance moved in the direction of the force (Figure 14.2):

$$\text{work} = \text{force} \times \text{distance} \quad \text{or} \quad \Delta W = F\Delta x$$

To work on the block, you need energy. You become tired and have less. What has happened to the energy?

The energy has not simply disappeared; it is inside the lead block. If you could examine the lead block microscopically after squashing, you would find that the molecules inside have been rearranged and that they are also vibrating a bit more vigorously. They have more energy. When you worked on the block, you transferred energy to it, which is now inside it. By working on the block, you increased its internal energy. The increase in the internal energy is equal to the work done on the block.

The symbol for internal energy is U. The increase in internal energy is given the symbol ΔU:

$$\text{increase in internal energy} = \text{work done on the block}$$

$$\Delta U = \Delta W$$

Electrical working

If you pass a current through the block of lead, this, too, will transfer energy to the lead. The power supply is applying a force to the electrons inside the lead, and moving them a distance in the direction of the force. This is **electrical working**. It also increases the internal energy of the lead.

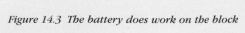

Figure 14.3 The battery does work on the block

Electrical working, like mechanical working, is an ordered process that is not driven by temperature difference. It is quite possible for energy to go from a cold power supply to a hot lead block, or from a low temperature to a high temperature. Again,

increase in internal energy = energy transferred by working

$$\Delta U = \Delta W$$

When a power supply does electrical work,

work done = power × time or $\Delta W = VI\Delta t$

Heating a lead block

- Leave a lead block to reach room temperature. Measure room temperature. Hold the block in your hands for a few minutes (Figure 14.4). Then measure its temperature.
- What has happened to the internal energy of the block?

Heating

As you know from Chapter 9, you can raise the internal energy of an object by **heating** it. If it is colder than your body temperature, all you need to do is to hold the block closely. You get a bit colder and the block gets a bit hotter. Energy goes from you to the block.

Again, the increase in internal energy of the block is equal to the energy transferred from you to the block. Energy transferred by heating is given the symbol ΔQ. When you heat an object,

increase of internal energy = energy transferred by heating

$$\Delta U = \Delta Q$$

Figure 14.4 Hold the block and observe the change in temperature

The difference between heating and working

In all three experiments above you transferred energy to the lead block. But the mechanism of transfer was quite different. In the first two situations, the energy was transferred by *working* on the block. In the third situation, it was by *heating*. Heating and working both transfer energy, but in a very important way they are different.

Working is an ordered process that has nothing to do with difference in temperature. It does not matter whether the lead block is hot or cold. You can still work on it by applying a force, and that force moving a distance, or by passing a current through it. Both will increase the internal energy of the lead block. Whatever temperature you are, you can still increase the internal energy of something by working on it.

As you read in Chapter 9, heating is a random process driven by temperature difference. Energy transfer only occurs from you to the object if you are hotter than the object (Figure 14.5). If the object is hotter than you are, the same process transfers energy from the object back to you (Figure 14.6).

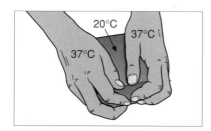

Figure 14.5 You heating an object

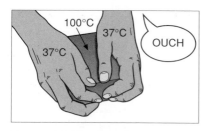

Figure 14.6 The object heating you

15 The first law of thermodynamics

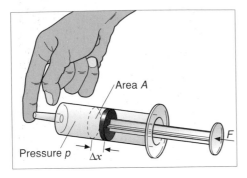

Figure 15.1 Work done = $F\Delta x = p\Delta V$

Work, pressure and volume

If you are working on a gas, it is convenient to calculate the work done from pressure and volume.

The gas in Figure 15.1 is being squashed with a force F moving a distance Δx. Therefore

$$\text{work done} = F\Delta x$$

The force F is acting over the area A. So from pressure $p = F/A$ we get

$$F = pA$$

so

$$\text{work done} = pA\Delta x$$

But $A\Delta x$ is the change in volume ΔV. So

$$\text{work done} = p\Delta V$$

$$\text{work done} = \text{pressure} \times \text{change in volume}$$

The first law of thermodynamics

The **first law of thermodynamics** states that energy is conserved. If you supply energy to a system by working and heating, the internal energy increases by the total amount of energy supplied. You can summarise the first law of thermodynamics by the equation:

increase in internal energy

   = energy gain by heating
      + energy gain by working (electrical or mechanical)

$$\Delta U = \Delta Q + \Delta W$$

Insulated situations

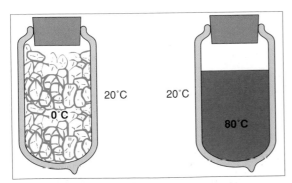

Figure 15.2 The flasks are isolated. Their contents neither gain energy from nor lose energy to their surroundings

If the vacuum flasks in Figure 15.2 are good insulators, it does not matter whether their contents are hot or cold – they are thermally isolated. They neither gain nor lose energy by heating.

If you apply the equation $\Delta U = \Delta Q + \Delta W$ to the contents, the energy transferred by heating, ΔQ, is zero. Therefore $\Delta U = \Delta W$.

If a system is at the same temperature as its surroundings, no heating takes place anyway, so again ΔQ is zero and $\Delta U = \Delta W$.

Complete isolation

There is no work being done either electrically or mechanically on or by the flasks in Figure 15.2. So ΔW is zero as well as ΔQ. If you apply the equation $\Delta U = \Delta Q + \Delta W$, you can see that ΔU is zero – there is no change in internal energy. The internal energy is constant.

The contents of the flasks are completely isolated from their surroundings, and so their internal energy is constant.

There are very few systems that are completely isolated from their surroundings. Bodies in space, like the Sun, are continuously losing energy by giving out heat. The Earth in space has roughly a constant temperature and constant internal energy because it is gaining energy from the Sun and also radiating an equal amount into space.

Perhaps the only really isolated system is the universe as a whole, which, so far as we are aware, is neither gaining energy from nor losing energy to anywhere else (Figure 15.3).

Figure 15.3 The internal energy of the universe is probably constant. It makes you wonder where the energy came from in the first place

Worked example

A 100 W filament lamp takes 200 ms to reach full brightness. Show how the equation $\Delta U = \Delta Q + \Delta W$ may be applied to the filament (a) during the first 0.001 ms after it is switched on and (b) after it has been switched on for some time.

(a) The filament takes 200 ms to reach full brightness. So in 0.001 ms, the temperature rises a little, but insufficient to heat its surroundings. During this time the power supply is working on the filament because a current is flowing through the filament. So ΔW is positive. The filament is still very nearly at the same temperature as its surroundings. So no heating is going on: ΔQ is zero. The work done by the power supply is used to raise the internal energy. $\Delta U = \Delta W$, and ΔQ is zero. Figure 15.4 summarises this situation.

(b) After the lamp has been switched on for some time, it has reached a steady operating temperature. If its temperature is steady, its internal energy is not changing. So ΔU is zero. Since $\Delta U = \Delta Q + \Delta W$, then $0 = \Delta Q + \Delta W$. Again, ΔW is positive. The power supply is still working on the filament. This means that ΔQ must be negative. So the energy gained by the filament by heating is negative: the filament is losing energy by heating. The filament is now heating the surroundings because, at its operating temperature, it is now hotter than the surroundings. Figure 15.5 summarises this situation.

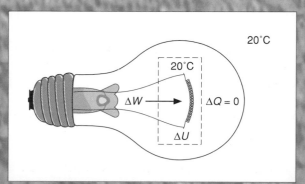

Figure 15.4 When the filament is at room temperature, all the work done by the power supply increases its internal energy

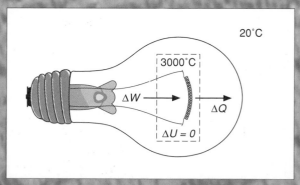

Figure 15.5 When the filament is at operating temperature, the work done by the power supply is equal to the energy lost by the filament heating the room

16 Molecular kinetic and potential energy

Molecules and oscillators

The molecules in a solid cannot change position, but they can vibrate. In many ways they behave like little bodies performing simple harmonic motion. To understand internal energy for a solid, it helps to study energy changes for a larger oscillating system.

Energy against time for an oscillator

- Use a motion sensor to produce a velocity–time graph for an oscillating trolley as shown in Figure 16.1.
- From the velocity–time graph, produce a kinetic energy–time graph.
- Predict the shape of the potential energy–time and total energy–time graphs.

Figure 16.1 Use the motion sensor to find how velocity varies with time

Energy–time graphs

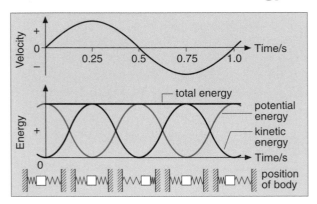

Figure 16.2 There is a constant interchange between kinetic and potential energy in an oscillator

The velocity–time graph in Figure 16.2 is for a body oscillating with period 1 s. The velocity–time graph is a sine wave. The velocity is zero at the beginning of the cycle, maximum positive 0.25 s later, zero half-way through the cycle at $t = 0.5$ s, maximum negative at 0.75 s and back at zero again at $t = 1$ s.

The red graph shows how kinetic energy varies. Kinetic energy $= \frac{1}{2}mv^2$: it is zero at $t = 0$, $t = 0.5$ s and $t = 1.0$ s, when the velocity is zero. Kinetic energy is maximum at $t = 0.25$ s, when the velocity is maximum positive, and also at $t = 0.75$ s, when the velocity is maximum negative.

The kinetic energy of the oscillator is a maximum when it is in the centre of its motion. A quarter of a cycle later, the kinetic energy is zero when the body is at one or other extreme of the motion.

The oscillator has potential energy stored in the compressed and stretched springs. The blue graph of Figure 16.2 shows how the potential energy varies with time. The potential energy is maximum at the extremes of the motion, and minimum in the middle.

The purple graph of Figure 16.2 is the total energy. It is the sum of the kinetic and potential energies. Energy is conserved. The graph is a horizontal straight line because the total energy of the oscillator remains constant.

Energy–displacement graphs

Figure 16.3 shows how the energy of an oscillator varies with the displacement. The blue graph shows the potential energy: it is zero in the centre of the motion and maximum when the displacement is maximum. The energy stored in a spring is proportional to the square of the extension: energy $= \frac{1}{2}kx^2$, where k is the spring constant and x is the displacement. For this reason, the energy–displacement graph for an oscillator has the (parabolic) shape of a $y \propto x^2$ graph.

The purple graph in Figure 16.3 is the total energy – the sum of the kinetic energy and the potential energy. The sum of kinetic and potential energy is constant, so the graph is a horizontal straight line.

The red graph in 16.3 shows how kinetic energy varies with displacement. The kinetic energy of an oscillator is zero at the extremes of the motion, when the velocity is zero, and a maximum in the centre of the motion.

Figure 16.4 shows how energy varies for a mass executing small vertical oscillations on the end of a spring. The gravitational potential energy obviously increases from bottom to top. The energy stored in the spring decreases from bottom to top, provided the oscillations are small and the spring is always slightly stretched even at the top. Again, the kinetic energy is maximum in the middle and zero at top and bottom.

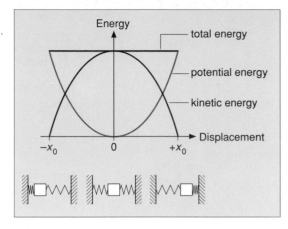

Figure 16.3 *Kinetic energy is a maximum in the centre, where potential energy is zero*

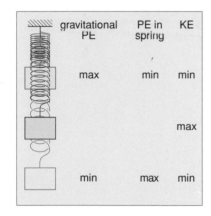

Figure 16.4 *When a mass oscillates vertically on a spring, some of its potential energy is in the spring, and some is due to gravity*

Oscillating molecules

The internal energy of a solid depends on the energy of its vibrating molecules. The molecules sometimes have kinetic energy and sometimes have potential energy. On average, half their energy is kinetic and half is potential. So the internal energy of a solid has both kinetic and potential energy components. If you increase the temperature of a solid, you increase both the kinetic energy and the potential energy of the molecules.

The internal energy of gases

You read in Chapter 8 that temperature is defined as that quantity which is proportional to the internal energy of an ideal gas. Atomic potential energy is due to forces between the atoms. In an ideal monatomic gas, there are no forces between the atoms, so there is no atomic or molecular potential energy. So the internal energy of an ideal gas is only kinetic.

In real gases, there are forces between the atoms and molecules. So the internal energy of a real gas is both potential and kinetic.

Energy sources

Primary energy

In the UK we use about 10^{19} J of energy each year. Approximately a third of this energy is used in industry, a third for transport and a third of it in our homes.

The raw sources of this energy are called **primary energy sources**. Figure 17.1 shows the primary energy sources for the UK during 1985. Natural gas is the only primary source that is used in homes, mainly for heating and cooking. Crude oil has to be processed before it is used, and few homes nowadays use coal.

The single greatest use of our primary energy sources is for electricity generation. In hydroelectricity, water drives turbines directly. The other major primary sources are used to boil water to produce steam, which drives turbines. You can read more about power stations in Chapter 19.

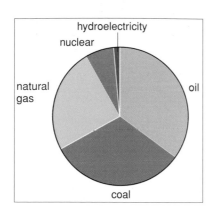

Figure 17.1 Primary energy sources in the UK for 1985

Fossil fuels

Long ago, plants grew in the sunlight. Then, as now, plants used energy from the Sun to split apart carbon dioxide (CO_2) found in the atmosphere. They released the oxygen into the atmosphere and used the carbon to build themselves up. The plants grew, withered and died; the plant material was covered, squashed and fossilised. Similarly, in the seas, countless tiny animals thrived and died. They, too, were covered and squashed, this time by marine sediments, which hardened into rocks under the high-pressure and high-temperature conditions that occur under the sea-bed.

These plant and animal remains, compounds of hydrogen and carbon, are the **fossil fuels** (oil, coal and natural gas) that provide most of our primary energy. When burned – combined again with the oxygen of the air – they get hot and can be used to heat homes or to heat water to produce steam in a power station.

Nuclear fuels

Chapter 9 of *Matter and Waves* discussed how energy is released when a large nuclide absorbs a neutron and splits into smaller nuclides. This is called *nuclear fission* (splitting). A typical reaction involves the absorption of a neutron by a nucleus of uranium-235:

$$^{235}_{92}U + ^{1}_{0}n \rightarrow ^{141}_{56}Ba + ^{92}_{36}Kr + 3^{1}_{0}n + \text{energy released}$$

The absorption of a single neutron leads to three more being released, each of which can cause a further fission reaction. Figure 17.2 shows how this process can lead to a **chain reaction**.

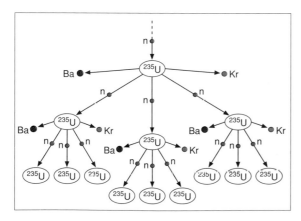

Figure 17.2 Each reaction emits more neutrons, which cause further reactions

Figure 17.3 shows a nuclear reactor. The **fuel rods** contain uranium isotopes. Neutrons produced when an element decays travel through the graphite **moderator**. This absorbs energy from the neutrons, slowing them down so that they are more easily absorbed by other uranium nuclei. Boron **control rods** absorb neutrons. They are raised or lowered to control the reaction, ensuring that, on average, only one of the three neutrons released from each decay is allowed to take part in a further fission.

The fuel rods and the moderator get hot as they absorb energy from the other fission fragments and the neutrons. Coolant is pumped around the fuel rods and through the moderator. This coolant then passes through a boiler, which produces steam.

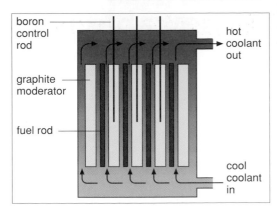

Figure 17.3 A nuclear reactor

Geothermal power

The radioactive isotopes in the ground fuel a natural nuclear reactor within the Earth's core which makes the core hot. Energy from this geothermal source can be extracted by pumping cold water several kilometres down into suitable rock outcrops such as granite. At the bottom, the water passes through cracks created by explosions in the hot rock. Heated water rises to the surface (Figure 17.4). Temperatures approaching 300°C can be achieved, sufficient to generate some electricity, although this hot water is mainly used for local heating.

There are a few working geothermal power stations where very hot springs occur naturally. But new geothermal power stations would create problems. The water pumped down would bring to the surface polluting salts, and the region of the Earth mined might cool down before it had returned the value of the original investment.

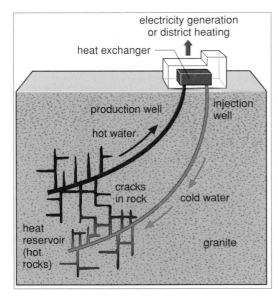

Figure 17.4 Water pumped down and then up extracts internal energy from the hot rock

Finite resources

The world has significant reserves of coal, oil, gas and nuclear fuel, but these reserves are limited. They are **finite resources**. The world's energy demand is rising ever more rapidly, and even with the most optimistic estimates of reserves demand for fuel will soon be greater than supply.

We are using up fossil fuels at a greater rate than they are being produced, and we run the risk of exhausting our reserves. Natural gas may last another 20 – 30 years, oil about twice as long, and nuclear fuel and coal may last over 100 years. Other resources like geothermal energy are also finite.

You might like to consider how the pie chart in Figure 17.1 might look this year compared with in 1985 when it was produced. How might it look in 20 or even 200 years' time?

Renewable resources

Hydroelectric power

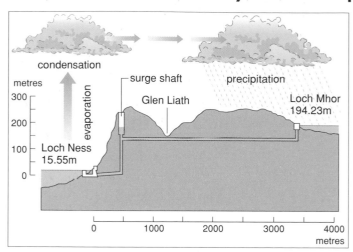

Figure 18.1 The Foyers hydroelectric scheme

Hydroelectricity is produced by harnessing naturally flowing water. Water leaves a high lake or reservoir, turns a turbine and generates electricity. The water used is replaced by rain falling on surrounding hills; the process is continuous, as shown in Figure 18.1. Hydroelectricity using natural lakes is a **renewable resource**: it is limitless. The Sun is continually evaporating water to make rain to refill the lakes feeding the turbines. Renewable sources offer some hope for our future energy needs because the source can be replenished as fast as it is being used.

Sadly, new hydroelectric schemes are not as attractive as they seem. The rotting flooded vegetation in a newly created lake produces as much greenhouse gas (in this case methane) as the equivalent fossil-fuel power station. And hydroelectric lakes gradually fill with silt. They are finite sources as well.

Figure 18.2 This wind farm has an output of 6×10^8 kW h

Winds and waves

Wind power is quite a promising renewable energy source. Large turbines fitted with propellers are turned directly by the wind and generate electricity (Figure 18.2). The costs of wind-generated electricity are nearly competitive with that from fossil fuels, and a small subsidy from the electricity generation industry is encouraging investment in the technology.

Sea waves are caused by winds as they blow over the sea surface. For some time the enormous energies of sea waves have seemed a promising energy source, but there has been little progress with wave power. The chief problem is that waves have such an enormous range of energies. Any generating system small enough to extract energy from average waves would be destroyed by the largest waves.

Biofuels

Biofuels involve obtaining energy from plants. You can burn plants as a fuel directly, use the methane gas from rotting vegetation, or burn the alcohol produced by fermenting plants. In Brazil, where land and sun are plentiful, sugar cane is grown as a biofuel and contributes significantly to the energy supply. In Britain, wood used to be a major energy source.

Energy from the Sun

Most of the energy that we use on Earth originates from the Sun. Plants need energy from the Sun for photosynthesis. If there were no plants there would be no biofuels and no fossil fuels. The Sun causes water to evaporate into the clouds, which leads to the rain upon which hydroelectric and other forms of water power depend. The Sun warms up the Earth's surface and its atmosphere by different amounts, setting up the pressure differences that lead to the air flows upon which wind and wave power depend.

The Sun's energy can be used directly for heating. Modern buildings in cold climates are designed to absorb and retain as much of the Sun's energy as possible during winter. They have large south-facing and small north-facing windows.

Solar panels use the Sun's energy to heat water (Figure 18.3). Solar radiation passes through the glass cover and is absorbed by the blackened collector plate. This conducts internal energy through the copper to water in thin pipes embedded in the plate.

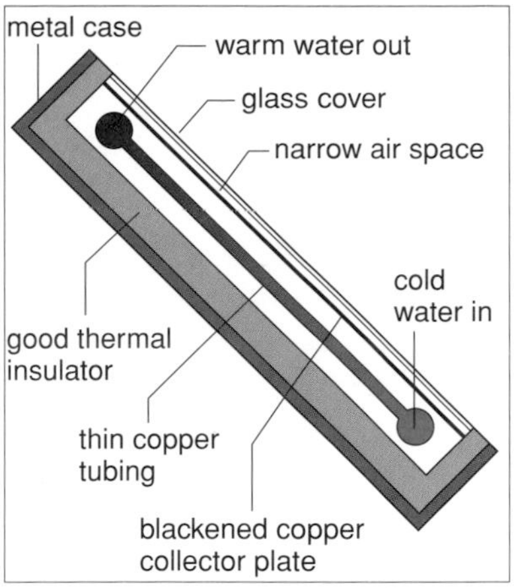

The Sun's energy can be used to generate electricity directly using a **photovoltaic cell** or solar cell. Figure 18.4 shows the structure of a silicon solar cell. When sunlight falls on its top surface, loosely held electrons are released, setting up a potential difference between the upper and lower metal contacts. The voltage produced is about 0.5 V, and a 60 cm^2 panel can develop a peak power of 1 W in bright sunlight. Solar cells are not economic energy sources at the moment.

Figure 18.3 The Sun's radiation heats the hot water in this solar panel

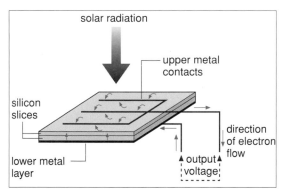

Figure 18.4 The Sun's radiation generates electricity in this silicon solar cell

The solar constant

Above the Earth's atmosphere, energy from the Sun arrives at a fairly constant rate. The **solar constant** (or solar flux) refers to the power of the Sun's rays falling normally on 1 m^2 at the top of the atmosphere. Its average value is about 1.4 kW m^{-2}. Only about 70% of the incident energy passes into the atmosphere; the rest is reflected away. The atmosphere itself absorbs some of this energy so that, at the equator, less than 1 kW m^{-2} falls on the Earth's surface on a bright sunny day. At the latitude of Britain, the midday flux is between 200 and 800 W m^{-2} on a clear day, depending on the season.

19 Heat engines

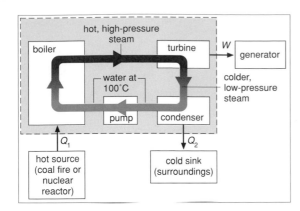

Figure 19.1 The power station uses a temperature difference to do work

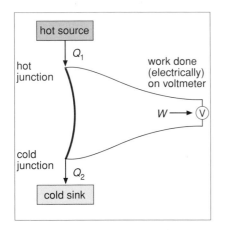

Figure 19.2 The thermocouple uses a temperature difference to do work

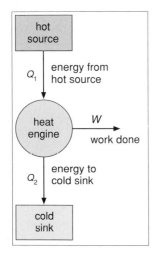

Figure 19.3 Heat input from hot source = work done by engine + heat given to cold sink

Thermal power stations

If you want to power a vacuum cleaner, a motor vehicle, or an industrial machine, you want to use your primary energy sources to do work.

A **heat engine** is a device that will take energy from a hot body and use it to do work. All thermal power stations – power stations that produce steam to drive turbines – make use of heat engines.

Figure 19.1 shows a block diagram of a thermal power station. The boiler, heated by gas, oil, coal or nuclear fuel, produces steam at high pressure. The steam passes through the turbine, forcing the blades to rotate, which turns the generator, producing electricity.

Turbines are designed to use as much energy as possible from hot, high-pressure steam. But they still give out waste low-pressure steam that is still quite hot. That steam is taken to a condenser, which turns it back into water, giving out latent heat. This waste energy is given out to the atmosphere. The liquid water is then pumped back into the boiler to be turned to high-pressure steam again.

There are three important energy flows in a power station. The first is Q_1, the energy taken by heating from the hot source, which heats the boiler. The second is W, the work done by the turbine on the generator. The third is Q_2, the energy given by heating from the condenser to the cool atmosphere.

Another common heat engine is the internal combustion engine, but there are others, for instance the thermocouple in Figure 19.2.

All heat engines take energy from a hot source. They cannot use all of this to do work, only a part. The rest of the energy they give out by heating to something cold, called a cold sink.

Efficiency of a heat engine

Applying the law of conservation of energy to the heat engine (Figure 19.3), we get:

energy from hot source = work done + energy given to cold sink
$$Q_1 = W + Q_2$$

which can be rewritten as

$$W = Q_1 - Q_2$$

The efficiency of a heat engine is the ratio of W, the work done by the engine, to Q_1, the energy taken by heating from the high-temperature source. So

$$\text{efficiency} = W/Q_1 = (Q_1 - Q_2)/Q_1 = 1 - Q_2/Q_1$$

There is always some energy flow to the cold sink; Q_2 cannot be zero. So a heat engine can never be 100% efficient.

Theoretical efficiency of a heat engine

It can be shown that the maximum efficiency of a heat engine depends on the Kelvin temperatures T_1 of the hot source and T_2 of the cold sink (Figure 19.4):

$$\text{maximum efficiency} = 1 - T_2/T_1$$

Only if the temperature of the sink T_2 is 0 K could the efficiency be as high as 100%. For thermal power stations, the sink temperature has a minimum of 373 K (= 100 °C, the boiling point of water). Turbine designers are constantly looking for higher-temperature materials so that they can raise the source temperature to increase the efficiency.

Today's turbines operate at about 600 °C (873 K). So for them

$$\text{maximum efficiency} = 1 - T_2/T_1 = 1 - 373/873 = 57\%$$

In practice, efficiencies are about 40%.

Heat pumps

If you put a hot body next to a cold body, energy flows from hot to cold. If you connect a heat engine between a hot and a cold body, the engine uses the temperature difference to do work.

Internal energy flows naturally from hot to cold. A heat pump can pump energy from cold to hot. It works the opposite way round from a heat engine. Mechanical work W is done on it; it takes energy Q from the cold body and gives energy $Q + W$ to the hot body (Figure 19.5). Refrigerators, freezers and air conditioners use heat pumps to pump internal energy from cold to hot.

Energy spreading around

You learned in Chapter 11 of *Matter and Waves* that an oscillator subject to resistive forces gradually leaks energy to its surroundings. The friction acting on moving surfaces and between the oscillator and the air transfers energy to the surroundings. If this energy is not replaced, the oscillations eventually stop.

At the beginning, the oscillator was a relatively concentrated energy store. At the end, the energy has been spread around and has increased the internal energy of the surroundings.

The natural tendency is for all concentrated stores of energy to become spread out. Our primary energy stores become smaller: the energy they have is dissipated as internal energy. In our universe, the stars become colder and the temperature differences are reduced. The universe's temperature differences do work. They are even the power sources for life. So as the fires of the universe die out, so will life, if things get that far!

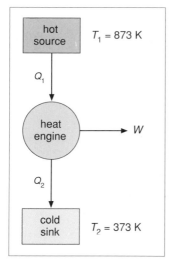

Figure 19.4 Efficiency of a heat engine = $1 - T_2/T_1$

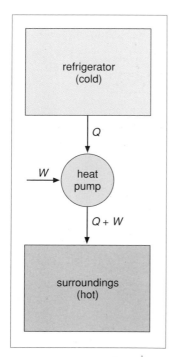

Figure 19.5 A heat pump pumps internal energy out of the refrigerator into the hotter surroundings

Electronics Topic

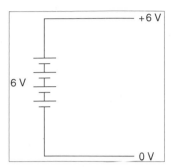

Figure E1 The voltage at the top of the battery is +6V

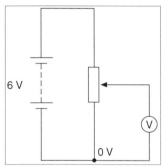

Figure E2 The voltage at the slider can vary from 0V to +6V

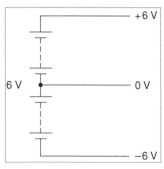

Figure E3 These batteries produce +6V and –6V relative to 0V

Voltage and voltage difference

You should remember from *Mechanics and Electricity* about the voltage between two points and how to measure it with a voltmeter. The battery in Figure E1 has a voltage difference of 6V across its terminals. In electronic circuits, it is useful to be able to talk about the *voltage at a point*. If you call the negative terminal of the battery in Figure E1 zero volts (0V), the voltage of the positive terminal is +6V.

Controlling voltage with potentiometers

Figure E2 shows a potentiometer connected to the same battery. The potentiometer can produce a range of voltages at its slider, from the voltage at the negative end (0V) to the voltage at the positive end (+6V).

Many electronics circuits use a supply that gives both positive and negative voltages. The two batteries in Figure E3 produce +6V and –6V relative to 0V. The supply is referred to as ±6V.

You studied potentiometers in Chapter 34 of *Mechanics and Electricity*. In Figure E4, the potentiometer connected between +6V and –6V can produce any voltage in between according to the position of the moveable contact.

The voltage produced by the potentiometer in Figure E5 is controlled automatically by illumination, not by manual movement of a slider. When the light-dependent resistor (LDR) is illuminated, the light produces free charge carriers in the LDR; this causes its resistance to decrease. So the voltage at the junction of the LDR and the fixed resistor increases. In the dark, the voltage at the junction is low.

You can also use switches and thermistors to make potentiometers that produce variable voltages. In Figure E6, V_{OUT} is high (+6V) when the switch is closed, and low (–6V) when the switch is opened.

Figure E7 has a thermistor. The thermistor's resistance is low when it is hot, when it has more charge carriers. When the thermistor is hot, V_{OUT} is high. When the thermistor is cold, V_{OUT} is low.

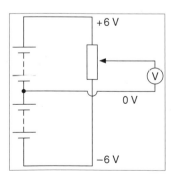

Figure E4 The potentiometer can produce any voltage between +6V and –6V

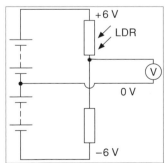

Figure E5 When the LDR is dark, the voltage at the junction with the resistor is low

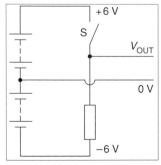

Figure E6 V_{OUT} is low (–6V) when the switch is opened

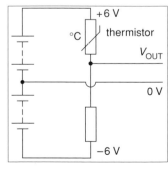

Figure E7 When the thermistor is hot, V_{OUT} is high

The operational amplifier

Many circuits in this Topic use the operational amplifier, or op-amp. Figure E8 shows two different types of op-amp and their circuit symbol.

The op-amp operates between positive and negative supplies. It has five connections:

- Two power supply connections, one positive and one negative.
- Two inputs, the inverting input (labelled '–') and the non-inverting input (labelled '+').
- An output.

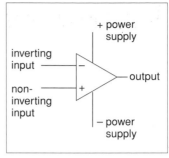

Figure E8 *Two op-amps and the symbol for an op-amp*

In Figure E9 the op-amp is connected to a power supply. The positive supply terminal of the op-amp is connected to +6V. The negative supply terminal is connected to –6V. In the circuits that follow, the power supplies are ±6V. But in practice power supply voltages can vary from ±1.5V or less to ±30V or more.

The inputs to the op-amp can be positive or negative voltages. The op-amp compares the voltages on the two inputs. The voltage on the non-inverting input is always called V_+. The voltage on the inverting input is always called V_-. So the op-amp compares V_+ with V_-. In Figure E9, V_- is kept constant at 0V, while the potentiometer controls V_+ between +6V and –6V.

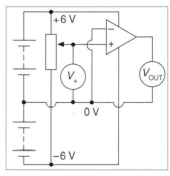

Figure E9 *V_- is kept constant at 0V, while the potentiometer controls V_+ between +6V and –6V*

The range of the op-amp output

The output of the op-amp behaves as if it were connected to an electronic potentiometer inside the op-amp. The power supply (±6V in this case) is connected across the potentiometer (Figure E10) and defines the possible range of output voltages. When the output of the op-amp is as high (positive) as it can get, it is said to be *saturated positively*. When the output is as negative as it can get, the output is said to be *saturated negatively*. Saturation typically occurs about 1V away from the supply voltages: ±5V with a ±6V supply, ±14V with a ±15V supply.

The input voltages (V_+ and V_-) act on the electronic circuit inside the op-amp and control the electronic slider of the potentiometer, and so control the value of the output voltage within the limits set by the power supply.

When V_+ is greater than V_- ($V_+ > V_-$), the output slider is at the top of the potentiometer and the output is as high as it can get, about +5V on a ±6V supply, as shown in Figure E10.

When V_+ is less than V_- ($V_+ < V_-$), as in Figure E11, the slider is at the bottom and the output is as low as it can get, about –5V on a ±6V supply.

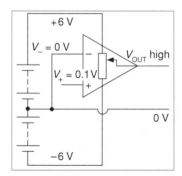

Figure E10 *When ($V_+ > V_-$), V_{OUT} is high*

Input currents

The electronic circuit inside the op-amp draws almost no current from either of the two inputs. So you can assume that no current flows into or out of either input of the op-amp.

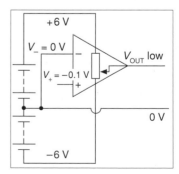

Figure E11 *When ($V_+ < V_-$), V_{OUT} is low*

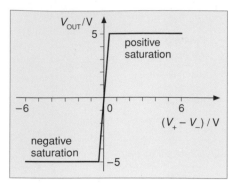

Figure E12 The transfer characteristic of the op-amp

The transfer characteristic of the op-amp

The output of the op-amp depends on the difference between the inputs, $(V_+ - V_-)$. When $(V_+ - V_-)$ is positive, the output is positive. When $(V_+ - V_-)$ is negative, the output is negative. Figure E12 shows how the output varies with $(V_+ - V_-)$. This graph is called the *transfer characteristic* of the op-amp.

The op-amp is called a *differential* amplifier because the output depends on the difference between the inputs. When V_+ is just less than V_-, $(V_+ - V_-)$ is small and negative. The output is then saturated negatively. If V_+ increases fractionally so that $(V_+ - V_-)$ is small and positive, the output is then saturated positively. This steep, but not quite vertical, line on the graph shows that even a small change in $(V_+ - V_-)$ causes a large change in V_{OUT}. The slope of the line is about 100 000 (10^5). This means that, for a change of $1\mu V$ in $(V_+ - V_-)$ in that region, the output changes by about $100\,000\,\mu V$, which is $0.1\,V$.

The slope of the line is called the *open-loop gain* A_{OL}: *A* stands for amplification or gain; the expression 'open-loop' means that there is no connection between the output and the input, which you will understand better after studying later circuits.

Across the steep region of the graph, the output voltage (V_{OUT}) is proportional to the difference in the input voltages ($V_+ - V_-$):

$$V_{OUT} = \text{constant} \times (V_+ - V_-)$$

The constant of proportionality is the gain A_{OL}. For a perfect op-amp,

$$V_{OUT} = A_{OL} \times (V_+ - V_-)$$

$$\text{gain} = A_{OL} = V_{OUT}/(V_+ - V_-)$$

It is convenient to regard $(V_+ - V_-)$ as the input to the circuit. So

$$\text{gain} = A_{OL} = \text{output/input}$$

The op-amp is a high-gain amplifier because A_{OL} is high.

Single-ended and dual-ended supplies

All the circuits so far show the op-amp with a dual-ended supply. This means a supply that has both positive and negative voltages. You can use an op-amp with a single-ended supply – just a positive supply – but if you do, the op-amp output will be constrained between typically 1 and 5V with a 6V supply because of saturation (Figure E13).

There are two types of op-amp circuits to study. Comparators use the saturation part of the characteristic. Amplifiers use the part of the characteristic where $(V_+ - V_-)$ is small and the output is not saturated.

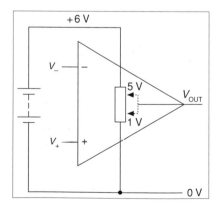

Figure E13 With a single-ended power supply, the output is constrained to positive voltages

Comparators

Comparators are op-amp circuits that use the saturated parts of the op-amp's characteristic to compare the two input voltages. If the output is high, it shows that V_+ is greater than V_-. If the output is low, it shows that V_+ is less than V_-.

Figure E14 is a comparator. In this circuit, V_- is fixed at 0 V. V_+ is controlled by the potential divider made by the LDR and resistor R.

- When the LDR is illuminated, its resistance is low. So V_+ is higher than 0 V, and therefore higher than V_-. So V_{OUT} is high and the lamp lights.
- When the LDR is dark, its resistance is high. So V_+ is lower than 0 V, and therefore lower than V_-. So V_{OUT} is low and the lamp is off.

This circuit could be used in any situation where it is possible or desirable to detect light relative to dark, for example lighting the lamp when the LDR is illuminated by the flames of a fire.

Reversing the action of a comparator

In Figure E15, the LDR and the fixed resistor R have been interchanged.

- When the LDR is illuminated, its resistance is low. But since the LDR is at the bottom of the potential divider, this time V_+ is lower than 0 V, and therefore lower than V_-. So V_{OUT} is low and the lamp is off.
- When the LDR is dark, its resistance is high. So V_+ is higher than 0 V, and therefore higher than V_-. So V_{OUT} is high and the lamp is on.

This circuit could be used as an automatic reading lamp. When the Sun goes down and the illumination gets too low, the lamp lights up.

This circuit and the previous one behave in exactly opposite ways: in one, the lamp lights in the dark; in the other, the lamp lights in the light. To swap over the circuit behaviour, the LDR and fixed resistor have simply swapped places. There are two other ways of swapping over the behaviour of comparator circuits. The circuit in Figure E16 behaves in the opposite way to the circuit in Figure E15 because its inputs are the opposite way round. Another swap can be arranged by connecting the lamp between V_{OUT} and the positive supply. This way the lamp will light when V_{OUT} is low. Figure E17 is the same as Figure E14, apart from the connection of the lamp. So the circuit of Figure E17 lights the lamp when the LDR is dark.

A comparator can use a single-ended power supply, but you need to provide a reference voltage for one of the inputs. In Figure E18 the potentiometer P provides a reference voltage for V_-. The potentiometer can vary this voltage and control the light level at which the circuit will switch the light on.

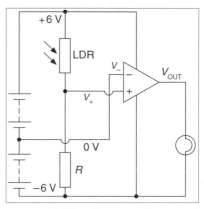

Figure E14 When the LDR is illuminated, the lamp lights

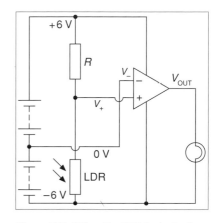

Figure E15 When the LDR is dark, the lamp lights

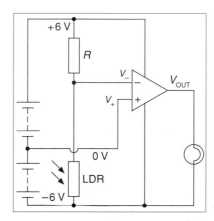

Figure E16 This circuit reverses the behaviour of Figure E15, because its input connections are reversed

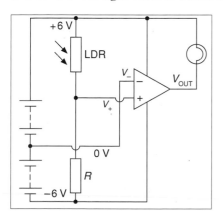

Figure E17 Changing the output connection is another way of reversing the circuit behaviour

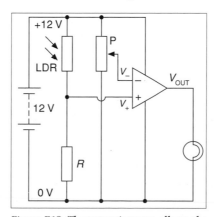

Figure E18 The potentiometer allows the switching level to be set

ELECTRONICS TOPIC

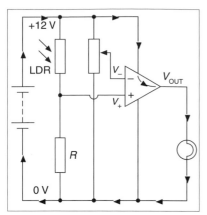

Figure E19 The current through the lamp comes from the power supply, via the op-amp

Current flow in a comparator circuit

In Figure E19 the current that flows through the op-amp's output comes from the power supply, through the op-amp, through its output, through the lamp and then back to the power supply. No current flows into or out of the inputs of the op-amp.

In some situations, for instance in the circuit of Figure E17, a current can flow from the power supply, through the lamp, and then *into* the output of the op-amp. Then it goes through the negative power supply connection and back to the power supply.

Low- and high-power op-amps

The small op-amp in Figure E8 is a low-power op-amp. It cannot control much current through its output. It can light a small lamp, but not a large one. Low-power op-amps are used for measuring and control circuits, which only need small currents.

The bigger op-amp is a high-power device. It can supply several amps, enough to power a larger lamp or a small motor.

Using LEDs

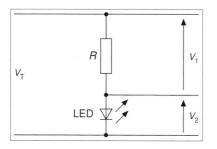

Figure E20 $V_T = V_1 + V_2$

Instead of using a lamp to indicate the state of the op-amp output, you can use a light-emitting diode (LED). An LED behaves like an ordinary diode, but it gives out light when current flows through it. Red LEDs need about 1.8V across them to give out light. Green and blue LEDs need larger voltages. When you use an LED you need a resistor in series with it to control the current through the LED.

Figure E20 shows an LED and a resistor connected to a voltage V_T. If V_T is 5V and the diode needs 1.8V across it, then the voltage across R will be 3.2V.

You calculate the value of R to control the current through the LED to give the brightness you want, subject to the maximum rated current of the diode. If the current needed is 20mA (typical for a low-power diode), then $R = 3.2V/20mA = 160\,\Omega$.

Amplifying

The voltage follower

Amplifiers use the sloping part of the op-amp transfer characteristic where $(V_+ - V_-)$ is small and the output is not saturated. Figure E21 shows the simplest amplifier. The input to the amplifier circuit is the voltage at the slider of the potentiometer. The output of the whole circuit is the op-amp output.

The inverting input of the op-amp is connected directly to the output of the op-amp. The input to the amplifier circuit is connected to the non-inverting input of the op-amp.

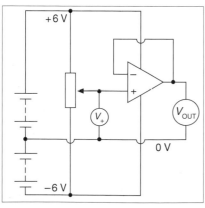

Figure E21 The unity-gain follower

For a good range of input voltages, the output voltage is equal to the input voltage. The output voltage follows the input voltage. Thus since

$$V_{OUT} = V_{IN}$$

$$\text{gain} = V_{OUT}/V_{IN} = 1$$

and so this circuit is called a *unity-gain follower*.

How the unity-gain follower works

You already know that when V_+ is more than a little greater than V_-, the output of the amplifier is large and positive; and if V_+ is less than V_-, the output of the amplifier is large and negative. In the circuit of Figure E21, if the output goes more positive than V_+, this makes V_- greater than V_+ as well, driving the output back down again. Similarly, if the output goes more negative than V_+, this makes V_- less than V_+ as well, driving the output back up again. This process, where a signal from the output contrarily controls the input, is called *negative feedback*.

The feedback forms a closed loop between the output and the input. The gain of the circuit is called the *closed-loop gain* A_{CL}, which in this circuit is 1.

The unity-gain follower gives the same output as its input. At first, you might think that it has little use. But the unity-gain follower draws no current from its input, but its output can give quite a large current. So you can use a unity-gain follower to make a voltmeter that draws no current from its supply. This is useful.

It is often convenient not to draw the power supplies in op-amp circuits, and merely to draw the other components and connections. Figure E22 shows Figure E21 without the power supplies. But remember that the power supplies are essential and must be there, even if they are not drawn in diagrams.

The coulombmeter

A voltmeter that draws no current can measure the voltage across a capacitor without discharging the capacitor. In Figure E23, you charge the capacitor from the potentiometer. The left-hand voltmeter measures the voltage to which the capacitor has been charged. When you connect the capacitor to the input of the unity-gain follower, the right-hand voltmeter measures the voltage across the capacitor, and the capacitor does not discharge, even though it is disconnected from the charging voltage.

In Figure E24 the voltmeter measures the voltage V across the capacitor C. The instrument is a coulombmeter, an instrument for measuring charge Q, which is given by

$$Q = CV$$

If you hold a negatively charged polythene strip near the lead shown, it will repel electrons onto the top plate of the capacitor. The voltmeter will read a negative voltage showing that the top plate of the capacitor is charged negatively.

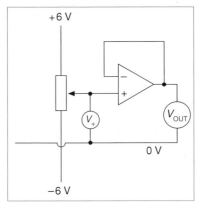

Figure E22 Even though the power supplies are not drawn, they are still needed

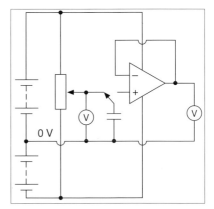

Figure E23 This op-amp circuit measures the voltage across the charged capacitor

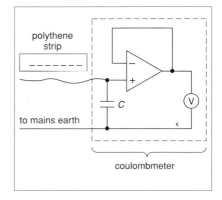

Figure E24 Charge = capacitance × voltage

ELECTRONICS TOPIC

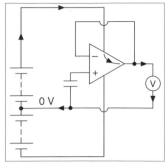

Figure E25 The voltmeter current comes from the power supply, not from the capacitor

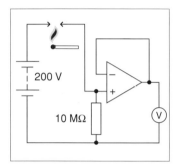

Figure E26 The flame causes the air to conduct

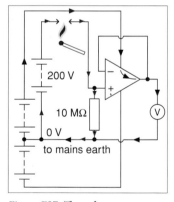

Figure E27 The voltmeter current comes from the power supply

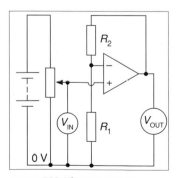

Figure E28 The non-inverting amplifier

Even though the power supplies in the previous circuit are not drawn, they are there. They provide the current through the voltmeter. Figure E25 shows the current flow if the input to the unity-gain follower is positive (and its output is positive).

The nanoammeter

You can also use the unity-gain follower to measure small currents. The nanoammeter, as its name suggests, measures currents down to the order of nanoamps ($1\,nA = 10^{-9}A$). To make a nanoammeter, use a unity-gain follower to measure the potential difference across a high-value resistor (Figure E26).

In this circuit the 200V power supply tries to drive a current through an air gap. When you hold a match under the gap, a current flows through the resistor. The unity-gain follower measures the voltage across the resistor, which is proportional to the current through the resistor.

The current that drives the voltmeter in the previous circuit comes from the battery that supplies the op-amp, as the large black arrows in the circuit in Figure E27 show. The current through the air gap is supplied by the 200V supply, and flows through a different loop, shown by the small red arrows.

The non-inverting amplifier

When you feed back all the output to the inverting input, the gain is 1. When, as in Figure E28, you feed only a proportion of the output to the inverting input, the gain is greater than 1. This circuit is called a *non-inverting amplifier*.

The potential divider formed by R_1 and R_2 determines the proportion of the output fed back. If you assume that the inverting input of the op-amp draws no current from the potential divider, the voltage at the inverting input is equal to $V_{OUT} \times R_1/(R_1 + R_2)$. If you assume that $V_+ = V_-$, this is the same as the voltage at the non-inverting input (i.e. the input to the whole amplifier circuit).

Since

$$V_{IN} = V_+ = V_{OUT} \times R_1/(R_1 + R_2)$$

then the gain is

$$A_{CL} = V_{OUT}/V_{IN} = (R_1 + R_2)/R_1 = 1 + R_2/R_1$$

To achieve a gain of 25, we must have $A_{CL} = 25 = 1 + R_2/R_1$. A useful guide is to make the smallest resistor, R_1, $10\,k\Omega$. Therefore,

$$25 = 1 + R_2/(10\,k\Omega)$$

$$24 = R_2/(10\,k\Omega)$$

$$R_2 = 240\,k\Omega$$

You can use the non-inverting amplifier to amplify alternating signals. In Figure E29 one trace of the double-trace oscilloscope monitors the input voltage, and the other the output voltage.

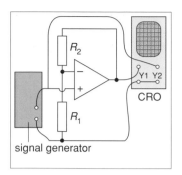

Figure E29 *You can use an oscilloscope to compare the input and the output*

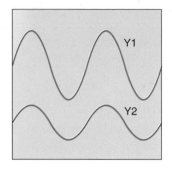

Figure E30 *The top trace is the output; the bottom is the input. This amplifier has a gain of 2*

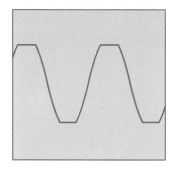

Figure E31 *Clipping distorts the output of an audio amplifier operating at high levels*

The top trace of Figure E30 shows the output of a particular non-inverting amplifier, and the bottom shows the input. If the sensitivity of the oscilloscope is set to the same value for both traces, the top trace has twice the amplitude of the bottom trace. This shows that the gain of the amplifier will be 2, and both R_1 and R_2 must have the same resistance.

If you increase the input voltage gradually, you will eventually get an output voltage like that in Figure E31. The output is limited by saturation and is clipped off at the saturation voltage. Clipping distorts the output of an audio amplifier operating at high levels; the output sounds as rough as it looks.

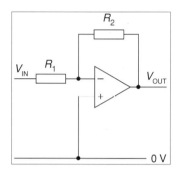

Figure E32 *The inverting amplifier*

The inverting amplifier

This is another kind of amplifier. The input is connected to the inverting input, giving different behaviour from that of the non-inverting amplifier. Figure E32 shows an inverting amplifier.

You can investigate the inverting amplifier by feeding in a small-amplitude sine wave to the input, and monitoring both the output and input with an oscilloscope. Figure E33 shows the output (top trace) of the inverting amplifier and the input (bottom trace), with $R_1 = 10\,\text{k}\Omega$ and $R_2 = 100\,\text{k}\Omega$. The output is ten times as large as the input, showing that the magnitude of the gain is 10. But the output is inverted relative to the input. When the output is positive, the input is negative, and vice versa.

The gain of this circuit is −10. The negative gain means that, when the input is positive, the output is negative, and vice versa. (It does not mean that the output is less than the input!)

You can work out a formula for the gain of the inverting amplifier, to understand why the gain of this circuit is −10 with the specified resistors.

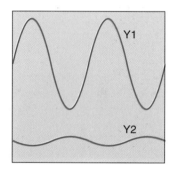

Figure E33 *Output and input for an inverting amplifier. The amplifier inverts the input signal*

Figure E34 shows the voltages and currents for an inverting amplifier. If the output is not saturated, then $V_+ = V_-$. But $V_+ = 0\,\text{V}$, and so $V_- = 0\,\text{V}$. The voltage across R_1 is V_{IN} and the voltage across R_2 is V_{OUT}. So

$$I_1 = V_{\text{IN}}/R_1 \quad \text{and} \quad I_2 = V_{\text{OUT}}/R_2$$

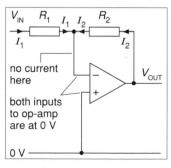

Figure E34 *Voltages and currents for an inverting amplifier*

ELECTRONICS TOPIC

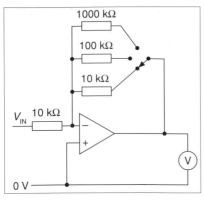

Figure E35 A switched-range voltmeter

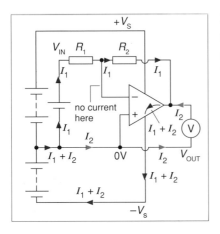

Figure E36 Current flow in an inverting amplifier. Current I_1 is shown with a red arrow, I_2 blue and $I_1 + I_2$ purple

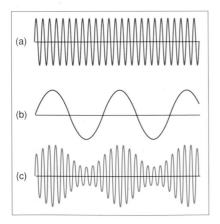

Figure E37 (a) A radio wave, (b) an audio wave and (c) the audio wave carried by the radio wave

The currents flowing into both inputs of the op-amp are zero, implying that $I_1 + I_2 = 0$. So

$$V_{IN}/R_1 + V_{OUT}/R_2 = 0$$
$$V_{IN}/R_1 = -V_{OUT}/R_2$$

and therefore

$$\textbf{gain} = V_{OUT}/V_{IN} = -R_2/R_1$$

Switched-range voltmeter

Figure E35 shows an inverting amplifier used as a *switched-range voltmeter*. With the switch in the position shown, the gain of the amplifier is –1, so the input voltage is numerically equal to the output voltage, and the voltmeter reads the negative of the input voltage.

If the switch is moved to select the 100 kΩ feedback resistor, the gain of the amplifier is –10. So the amplifier makes the voltmeter ten times more sensitive. If the switch is moved to select the 1000 kΩ feedback resistor, the voltmeter is 100 times more sensitive than without the amplifier.

In all positions of the switch, the top terminal of the voltmeter becomes negative if V_{IN} is positive. So to make a sensible voltmeter, we simply show the magnitude and reverse the sign again.

Figure E36 shows the flow of current in an inverting amplifier circuit. The current I_2 is the current that flows through the voltmeter. In this circuit, the input is positive, so the output is negative. Current flows into the output of the op-amp from the 0 V line after passing through the load. I_2 then flows with I_1 through the negative supply line, through the negative part of the power supply and then through the 0 V line. Then it flows back to the voltmeter.

Receiving

The sounds that you hear coming from a radio are audio-frequency (AF) signals. They cover the frequencies from about 15 Hz up to about 20 kHz. It is not practicable to transmit these signals directly as electromagnetic waves. So radio transmitters send out electromagnetic waves at higher (radio) frequencies, with the audio-frequency signals carried on top of the radio waves. Graph (b) in Figure E37 shows an audio-frequency signal and graph (a) is the radio-frequency (RF) signal that will carry it. Graph (c) shows the modulated radio-frequency wave – the RF wave combined with the AF wave. The RF wave is amplitude-modulated; its amplitude is modulated, or changed, in step with the AF wave.

Many different transmitters send out their own modulated RF signals, each carrying their own radio programme or other information. The transmitters near you all use different radio frequencies, and you choose the programme you want to listen to by choosing which radio frequency your radio selects.

Figure E38 shows a simple radio receiver. It picks up electromagnetic waves from the atmosphere, selects the right signal, detects the audio wave that the signal carries, smoothes that wave and then produces a sound wave that you can hear.

Electromagnetic waves from the transmitter produce an alternating voltage between the aerial and earth. The aerial and earth receive the signal, and the alternating voltage between them powers the rest of the circuit.

The coil is made by wrapping wire round a tube, or sometimes round a piece of magnetic material. The coil works together with the variable tuning capacitor. Together they form a tuned circuit, which selects the signal.

Figure E39 shows how the output from this tuned circuit depends on the frequency of the wave fed into it. At one particular frequency – the resonant frequency – the output from this circuit is a maximum. You adjust this circuit so that its resonant frequency is the frequency of the transmitter you wish to receive.

To receive a transmitter with a higher frequency, you can either decrease the number of turns of the coil, or reduce the capacitance of the tuning capacitor. For a lower selected frequency, you can either increase the number of turns of the coil or increase the capacitance of the tuning capacitor. Most radios have a variable capacitance and tune the signal by changing this. They also have a switch that connects in a different number of turns of wire on the coil for changing waveband. So large changes are accomplished by changing the coil, small ones by changing the tuning capacitance.

The voltage across the tuning capacitor is then like graph (a) in Figure E40. It is a modulated radio-frequency wave, just the same as graph (c) in Figure E37. The diode allows current to flow through in one direction only. It cuts the bottom of the wave, turning it from an alternating voltage to a bumpy direct voltage, as in graph (b), which follows the audio signal. The smoothing capacitor and resistor smooth the detected wave, turning it into a copy of the AF wave that was carried by the RF signal, as shown in graph (c). This signal drives the earpiece, and if the transmitter is powerful enough, you can hear a signal in the earpiece, powered directly from the RF signal transmitted through the air.

A receiver like this is called a crystal set. Its output will be very quiet, but crystal sets were the standard way of receiving radio signals when radio broadcasts first started.

You can make a crystal set, and if you live close to a transmitter it can provide an adequate signal for personal listening. If you want to drive a loudspeaker you need an audio amplifier to make the signal louder. The non-inverting amplifier in Figure E28 will do the job.

Commercial radio receivers have radio-frequency amplifiers as well as audio-frequency amplifiers, to amplify the signal before it is detected as well as afterwards.

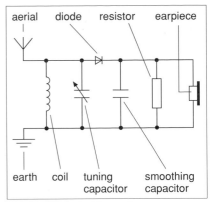

Figure E38 A simple receiver

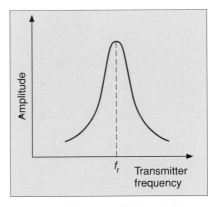

Figure E39 The output of the tuned circuit is a maximum at f_r

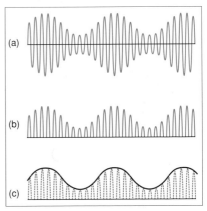

Figure E40 (a) The modulated radio wave, (b) the rectified modulated wave and (c) the smoothed, rectified wave, recovering the audio signal

Medical Physics Topic

X-rays for diagnosis and therapy

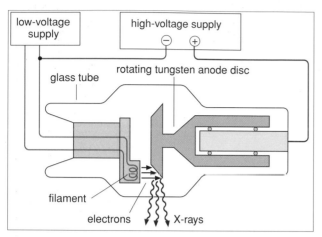

Figure M1 When electrons hit the anode, they give out X-rays

Making X-rays

X-rays are part of the electromagnetic spectrum; they are high-energy electromagnetic waves. Remember from *Matter and Waves* that photon energy depends on the Planck constant and frequency ($E = hf$). So X-rays also have a high frequency and therefore a short wavelength. X-rays are used for investigating illness (*diagnosis*) and treating it (*therapy*).

Figure M1 shows a typical X-ray tube. The low-voltage supply provides a current that heats the filament. This gets hot enough to emit electrons. The high-voltage supply makes the anode very positive with respect to the filament and attracts the emitted electrons. The electrons hit the anode at high speed, giving up their kinetic energy.

The design of the X-ray tube ensures that the electrons hit a small area on the anode. This area is the source of all the X-rays, which then spread out over a range of directions.

If the voltage between the filament and anode is 70 kV, the kinetic energy of the electrons is 70 keV. Since $1 \, eV = 1.6 \times 10^{-19} J$, for one electron we get

$$\textbf{electron energy} \; = \; 70000 \, \times \, 1.6 \, \times \, 10^{-19} J \; = \; 1.12 \, \times \, 10^{-14} J$$

If this electron gives up all its kinetic energy as an X-ray photon, then the energy of the photon is equal to the kinetic energy of the electron. So the X-ray photon energy is

$$E \; = \; hf \; = \; 1.12 \, \times \, 10^{-14} J$$

But we know the value of the Planck constant, $h = 6.6 \times 10^{-34} J s$. So the frequency of the X-ray photon is

$$f \; = \; E/h \; = \; (1.12 \times 10^{-14} J)/(6.6 \times 10^{-34} J s) \; = \; 1.7 \times 10^{19} Hz$$

You can also calculate the wavelength of the X-ray for this energy from the equation $c = f \lambda$. Rearranging gives

$$\lambda \; = \; c/f \; = \; (3.0 \times 10^8 m s^{-1})/(1.7 \times 10^{19} Hz) \; = \; 1.78 \times 10^{-11} m$$

The X-rays produced only have this wavelength if all the kinetic energy of the electrons hitting the anode becomes photon energy. In practice, most electrons give up only a proportion of their energy as X-ray photons. So the tube produces a range of X-ray energies, called a *spectrum*, with a maximum energy (maximum frequency and minimum wavelength) given by the calculation above.

In practice, too, most of the kinetic energy of the electrons ends up raising the temperature of the anode. For some X-ray tubes less than 1% of the electron's kinetic energy is released as X-rays. This is why the anode is made to spin, so the target area can cool down briefly during each revolution.

The effect of tube voltage

Figure M2 shows the spectra produced by a tungsten-anode X-ray tube with three different accelerating voltages. The area under the curve is a measure of the total intensity of the X-rays produced; it increases with increasing tube voltage. As you would expect, if the tube voltage increases, so does the maximum photon energy. What also increases is the photon energy at the peak of the curve, where the intensity is maximum.

In addition to the range of wavelengths, the spectra from X-ray tubes show lines that are characteristic of the anode material. Tungsten is the usual material for the anode because it has a high melting point. On the graphs for 100 kV and 200 kV you can see the characteristic lines of the tungsten spectrum.

You can see that, to increase the photon energy of X-rays, you increase the tube voltage, but to increase the intensity, you increase the current.

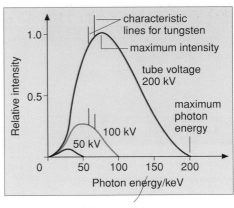

Figure M2 *If you increase the tube voltage, you increase intensity and photon energy*

The effect of tube current

Figure M3 shows the effect of keeping the X-ray tube voltage constant whilst changing the tube current. For both currents, the shape of the curves and the maximum photon energy are the same. For the larger current, the intensity is greater. A larger current means a larger number of electrons colliding with the anode per second, and so a larger number of X-ray photons are produced per second.

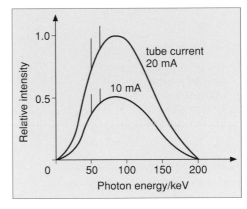

Figure M3 *If you increase the tube current, you increase the intensity alone*

X-ray absorption

X-rays interact with matter and are absorbed by four different processes: simple scattering, photoelectric absorption, Compton scattering and pair production.

Simple scattering occurs at low energy, when the energy of the X-ray photons is less than the binding energy of an electron (Figure M4). X-rays are scattered by the orbiting electrons of the matter through which they pass, without losing energy. Simple scattering is relatively unimportant with the higher energies of medical X-ray beams.

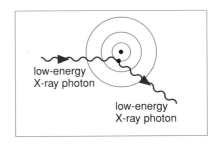

Figure M4 *In simple scattering, X-rays are scattered by orbital electrons without losing energy*

Photoelectric absorption (Figure M5) is the major mechanism for absorption of diagnostic X-rays. It occurs when the energy of the X-ray photons is more than the binding energy of an electron. An X-ray photon gives up all its energy to an electron. The electron is ejected from the atom in the same way that they are ejected in the photoelectric effect. The other electrons in the atom rearrange themselves and emit lower-frequency radiation. X-rays have much more energy than visible or ultra-violet light, so they can cause inner electrons to be emitted, as well as outer ones.

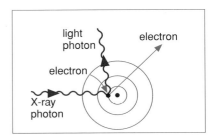

Figure M5 *In photoelectric absorption, all the X-ray photon energy ejects an electron.*

MEDICAL PHYSICS TOPIC

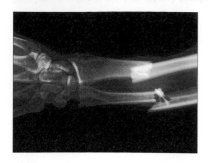

Figure M6 *Photoelectric absorption produces sharp shadows of bones*

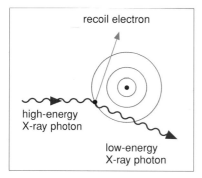

Figure M7 *In Compton scattering, part of the X-ray photon energy emits an electron*

Photoelectric absorption increases rapidly with the proton number, because atoms with larger proton number have more outer electrons. So atoms with large proton number absorb much more strongly. Calcium in bones absorbs much more than the hydrogen or oxygen atoms in the water of soft tissues. So bones cause dark shadows on X-ray films (Figure M6). Photoelectric absorption decreases with increasing X-ray photon energy.

Compton scattering takes over at still higher X-ray photon energies, when the photon energy is much more than the binding energy of the electrons. The incident X-ray photon is deflected and its energy is reduced (Figure M7). An outer electron, called the recoil electron, is emitted from the atom. Compton scattering decreases slowly with increase in photon energy. Compton scattering is not strongly dependent on proton number. For high-energy X-ray photons, where Compton scattering is the main reason for absorption, bone does not absorb much more than soft tissue.

Pair production is important when the X-ray photon energy is greater than about 1 MeV. A photon interacts with a nucleus, and produces an electron–positron pair.

Dependence of intensity on absorber thickness

A monochromatic beam of X-rays is a beam containing X-rays of a single frequency. When a *parallel* monochromatic beam goes through a material, its intensity is reduced. Intensity is measured in $W\,m^{-2}$. When a beam of initial intensity I_0 passes through a material of thickness x, the intensity is reduced to I according to the relationship

$$I = I_0 e^{-\mu x}$$

Here μ is called the *total linear attenuation coefficient*. It depends on the type of material and on the frequency of the X-rays; μ is measured in m^{-1}.

You can calculate the thickness of absorber that reduces the intensity from its initial value I_0 to half this value, $I_0/2$. This thickness is called the *half-value thickness* $x_{1/2}$. Substituting $I = I_0/2$ and $x = x_{1/2}$ in the previous equation:

$$I_0/2 = I_0 e^{-\mu x_{1/2}}$$
$$1/2 = e^{-\mu x_{1/2}}$$
$$2 = e^{\mu x_{1/2}}$$
$$\ln 2 = \mu x_{1/2}$$
$$x_{1/2} = (\ln 2)/\mu$$

X-rays spreading out from a *point* source obey the inverse square law: intensity $\propto 1/x^2$, where x is the distance from the source. If you double the distance from the source, the intensity quarters.

X-rays for diagnosis

Figure M8a shows how a radiograph is produced with X-rays. The tube emits X-rays, which pass through the patient's body and strike the photographic film. The film records the shadow of any object placed between it and the X-ray source. A point source of X-rays produces shadows with sharp edges. As Figure M8b shows, if the source of X-rays is wide, the shadow is fuzzy. You can see these effects for yourself by using a light bulb instead of the X-ray tube and a piece of card with a small hole in it.

X-rays and living cells

Most X-rays pass straight through living cells without affecting them. But when the X-rays do interact with a cell, they usually kill the cell. Our bodies can cope with losing a few cells with little effect. Occasionally, an X-ray can change a cell in such a way that it can still reproduce. A tiny proportion of these changes result in cancer cells – cells that grow and reproduce rapidly, without limit, and spread to other parts of the body.

Heterogeneous beams and filtration

The X-ray beams are heterogeneous. They are made up of a range of different photon energies from low to high. The low-energy X-rays are readily absorbed by the body. They do not even penetrate soft tissue to reach the photographic film. So they merely increase the X-ray dose to the patient without being useful for diagnosis. So X-ray beams are usually filtered before use by passing them through a few millimetres of aluminium. Figure M9 shows that filtration removes lower photon energies more than higher photon energies; it leaves the beam with a smaller spectral spread and a greater proportion of high-energy X-rays. These penetrate the patient's body more than low-energy X-rays, and for this reason the beam is said to be *harder*.

Diagnosis uses X-rays of energy up to about 160 keV. For these energies, the photoelectric effect is the main cause of absorption. Bone absorbs X-rays of these energies more strongly than does soft tissue, because it contains elements like calcium with a relatively high proton number compared with the carbon, oxygen and hydrogen in soft tissue. So bone shows up differently on the radiograph.

It is hard to distinguish some things, such as a cancerous growth from normal tissue, or the lining of the gut from the contents. In situations like these, the patient can be given an X-ray-absorbing dye to make the radiograph clearer. When examining the gut, a barium enema can coat the bowel wall to make it visible and show up ulcers or growths. Dyes can be used to make certain types of cancer more visible because the dyes are taken up more rapidly by cancerous cells than by normal cells because cancer cells grow faster.

Therapeutic X-rays

X-rays can be used in therapy, to treat cancer by killing the cancer cells. Because they grow faster, X-rays more readily kill cancer cells than normal cells. Much X-ray treatment of cancer is palliative – it provides relief of the effects, but does not get rid of the cancer completely and make a cure.

As stated above, low-energy X-rays are absorbed readily, even by soft tissue. They can be used for therapy, but only for shallow tumours. Most therapy

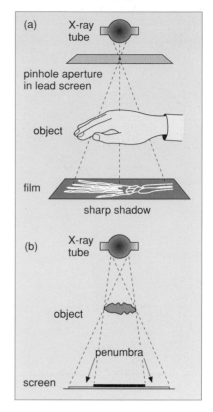

Figure M8 To get sharp X-ray photographs, you need a point source

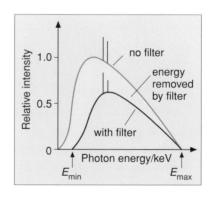

Figure M9 Filtration reduces the proportion of low-energy rays, so making the beam 'harder'

MEDICAL PHYSICS TOPIC

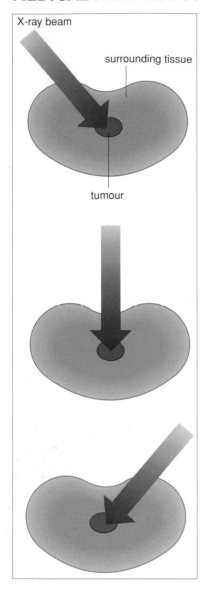

X-ray beam

surrounding tissue

tumour

Figure M10 The tumour receives the radiation all the time. The healthy flesh only receives some of the radiation

Table M1 *Some specific acoustic impedances*

Medium	Specific acoustic impedance /kg m^{-2} s^{-1}
air	0.000439×10^6
fat	1.38×10^6
water	1.50×10^6
brain	1.58×10^6
blood	1.59×10^6
muscle	$\sim 1.7 \times 10^6$
bone	$\sim 6 \times 10^6$

needs X-rays of higher energy, in the MeV region. These are produced by a linear accelerator, which accelerates electrons along a long path, or a betatron, which accelerates electrons in a circular path. High-energy X-rays are more penetrating, causing less damage to skin. In addition, the principal method of absorption is by Compton scattering and is not dependent on proton number; so they cause less damage to bones.

Planning X-ray treatment

For X-ray therapy you want the dose to be high enough to kill the cancerous tissue, but you want to do as little damage as possible to surrounding tissue. The dose is therefore critical. Too much will destroy healthy normal tissue; too little will not kill the cancerous tissue.

Radiographers give treatments with multiple beams (Figure M10). They direct X-rays at the tumour from a range of angles, each through different parts of the surrounding tissue. The tumour gets exposed all the time; the surrounding tissue only receives certain beams. The radiographer aims the beams accurately at the tumour, first marking the beam entry points permanently on the patient's skin. Sometimes a 'mask' is used, which is specially made to fit the patient and keep him/her still to ensure that the beam hits the required area.

Ultrasonics in medicine

Sound waves are longitudinal vibrations in a medium. You can hear frequencies up to about 20 kHz, but sound waves of much higher frequencies, called *ultrasound*, can be made. Ultrasound is a most useful medical tool for exploring the body. Medical ultrasonics works by sending out pulses of ultrasound and monitoring the echoes – this is the *sonar principle*. It is the same system that a bat uses for navigation.

Medical ultrasonics relies on a property of materials called the *specific acoustic impedance*. This is the speed of sound in a material multiplied by the density of that material. If ultrasound arrives at a boundary between two materials with different specific acoustic impedances, some ultrasound is reflected at the boundary. These reflections are analysed and give information about the structure of the body. The specific acoustic impedances for a number of materials are shown in Table M1.

Calculating the amount of sound reflected

On an ultrasound scan, the strength of the reflection at a boundary and the brightness with which it shows up depend on the specific acoustic impedances of the two media at the boundary. The ratio of the sound intensity reflected from the boundary (I_r) to the sound intensity incident on the boundary (I_i) is called the *intensity reflection coefficient* α. The value of α depends on Z_1 and Z_2, the specific acoustic impedances of the two media, and is calculated from

$$\alpha = I_r/I_i = (Z_2 - Z_1)^2/(Z_2 + Z_1)^2$$

To calculate the proportion of the intensity reflected at a boundary – for instance, between blood and brain – you substitute values in the equation:

$$\alpha = I_r/I_i = (Z_2 - Z_1)^2/(Z_2 + Z_1)^2$$
$$= (1.59 \times 10^6 - 1.58 \times 10^6)^2/(1.59 \times 10^6 + 1.58 \times 10^6)^2 = 9.9 \times 10^{-6}$$

Only a tiny proportion – about 10 millionths – of the sound intensity is reflected back from a boundary between blood and brain. This is why it is difficult to use ultrasound to examine the structure of the blood vessels in the brain. Strong reflections, where α is approximately 1, come from air/bone or blood/bone interfaces, where the acoustic impedances are very different.

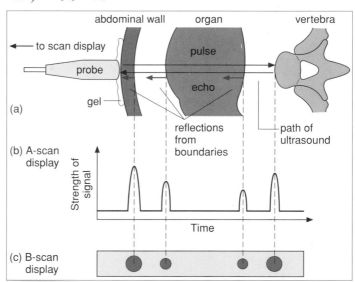

The principle of scanning

A short pulse, whose frequency is of the order of a few MHz, is applied to a transducer in a probe. This transmits a pulse of sound waves and then receives the reflections, as shown in Figure M11a. The layer of gel between the probe and the body is a coupling medium; it replaces the air layer, which would cause large reflections and stop the ultrasound getting into the body.

Figure M11 Reflections from boundaries can be displayed either as a graph (A-scan) or as spots of different brightness (B-scan)

Figure M11b shows an A-scan (amplitude scan), which is a graph of the strength of the reflected signal against time. From this graph, the radiographer can find the depth of the reflecting boundaries. A-scans are used to make precise measurements on the eye.

Figure M11c shows a B-scan (brightness scan). Compare it with the A-scan above. In the B-scan, the brightness of a spot of light on a display screen is proportional to the strength of the reflected signal.

Two-dimensional B-scans

A probe containing a number of transducers can sweep ultrasound pulses across an area of the body and produce individual B-scans at different angles. These can be assembled on the display to produce a cross-section of the part of the body

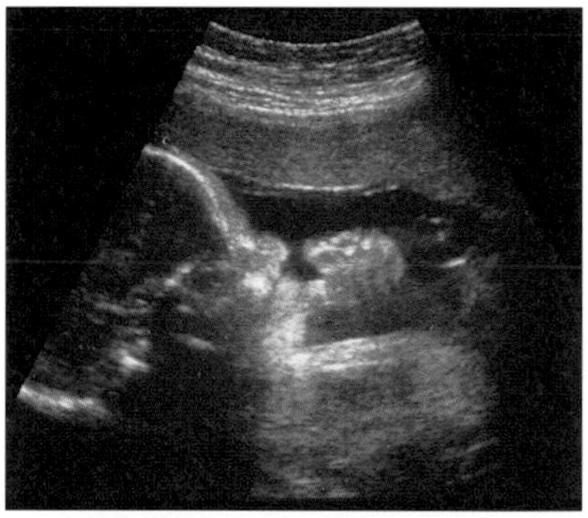

Figure M12 We are wonderfully made! A 12-week-old baby in the uterus

being scanned. Figure M12 shows a scan of a baby 12 weeks old in the uterus. The scans are repeated 25 times a second to produce a moving real-time image of what is being scanned.

Figure M13 shows a block diagram of an ultrasound scanner. The clock controls the whole system. The transmitter sends signals to the probe, which causes it to send out a single pulse. The receiver receives the pulse reflected at different times from different places at different

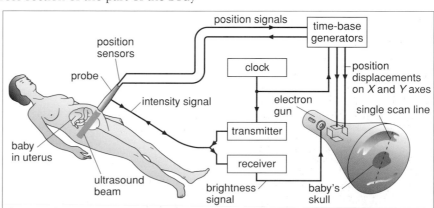

Figure M13 B-scanning. The electron gun sends the beam to a position on the screen corresponding with the source of the reflection. The brightness of the spot indicates the strength of reflection

intensities. The time delay shows how deep the boundary is; the position controller decides which direction it is; and the receiver controls the brightness. A sequence of reflections gives one line on the screen.

The resolution of ultrasound

The speed of ultrasound in tissue is typically around $1500\,\mathrm{m\,s^{-1}}$. At a frequency of 2 MHz, the wavelength is 0.75 mm. The wavelength limits the resolution and determines the smallest separation you can see. Because of diffraction effects, you cannot resolve things much smaller than the wavelength. For good resolution (i.e. to see tiny details), you want short wavelength and therefore high frequency.

Ultrasound waves are absorbed by the tissue through which they pass. The higher the frequency, the greater the attenuation or weakening of the signal. So, for good penetration, you want low frequency.

The choice of frequency is therefore a compromise between resolution and attenuation, leading to the use of frequencies between 2 and 10 MHz.

Doppler effect

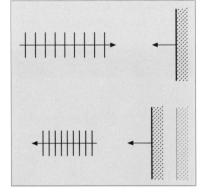

When ultrasound strikes a boundary that is moving *towards* the transmitter (Figure M14), each wavefront meets the moving boundary slightly before it would have done with a stationary boundary. So the reflected wavefronts are closer together than those striking the boundary, and the frequency of the reflected wave is higher. If the boundary is moving *away from* the transmitter, the frequency of the reflected wave is lower.

The frequency shift Δf in this situation is given by the equation

$$\Delta f = 2fv/c$$

Figure M14 If the reflecting boundary moves towards the transmitter, the wave length of the reflected wave is shorter

where f is the original frequency, v is the speed of the reflector and c is the speed of sound in the medium. By measuring the frequency shift in the reflected wave, you can work out the speed of a moving interface in the body.

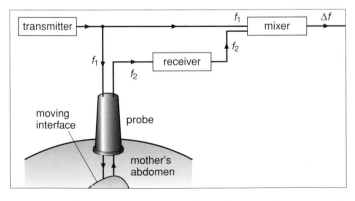

Figure M15 The mixer produces the difference between the transmitted and the reflected signals

Figure M15 shows a block diagram of a Doppler ultrasound system used to check on the blood supply to a baby in the womb. The probe transmits a signal at frequency f_1 and receives a reflected frequency of f_2. The mixer takes the transmitted and received signals and produces an output, which is the difference Δf.

A Doppler system can detect the shift in frequency of the weak reflections from the baby's blood flowing in the umbilical cord or in the large arteries of the heart to check that the blood flows are sufficient for proper growth and development.

Ultrasound compared with X-rays

Ultrasound imaging is safer than using X-rays. There are no known hazards connected with the low-power ultrasound used for scanning. But all X-rays have a chance of doing damage, whatever the dose. Both ultrasound and X-rays can produce real-time two-dimensional images, and they both expose the tissue for as long as observations are being made. Safety considerations mean that ultrasound is used routinely for these purposes and X-rays are used only when the comparatively high risk is justified by the benefits. For instance, if a patient is likely to die from cancer anyway, the extra dose of radiation hardly matters.

The penetration of ultrasound is limited, particularly where there are air/tissue or bone/tissue interfaces. So you cannot use ultrasound to investigate the chest cavity. But X-rays are poor at resolving soft tissues, so are not good for examining the organs of the abdomen. The wavelength of all X-rays is very much less than the shortest ultrasound wavelength. So the resolution of X-ray equipment can be much better than ultrasound.

The slow speed of ultrasound and the fact that it reflects from tissue means that you can get depth information directly from an ultrasound scan. So ultrasound produces sectional maps of reflection. Tissue boundaries do not reflect X-rays, and, even if they did, X-rays travel at the speed of light, so it would be difficult to measure the time delay. So to get depth information from X-rays you need to use *tomography* – taking a number of images from a range of angles to produce information about a cross-section. Ordinary X-rays are *projection* maps of transmission.

Nuclear medicine

Imaging with radio-nuclides

Many radioactive nuclides are used medically to investigate the body. Alpha (α) and beta (β) radiations from radio-nuclides in the body are absorbed within the body. But gamma (γ) rays are penetrating enough to leave the body, and so a gamma detector can trace the path of gamma emitters within the body. The radiographer chooses a chemical compound containing a gamma emitter that will be absorbed by the part of the body under investigation. For instance, radio-isotopes of iodine can be taken by mouth. They travel through the bloodstream and are absorbed by the thyroid gland. The emissions from the thyroid gland give information about how well it is working. Technetium ($^{99m}_{43}$Te) can be made into many different compounds to be absorbed by the brain, lungs, liver, bone, heart and circulatory system. The gamma emissions for these organs can be used to study their functions.

Radio-nuclides

Most medical radio-nuclides are prepared by neutron bombardment in a nuclear reactor. Iodine-131 (^{131}I) is an example of a radio-nuclide that is produced in this way. Tellurium-130 (^{130}Te) is placed in a nuclear reactor and under the intense bombardment eventually captures a neutron. The resulting nuclide then decays to ^{131}I by the emission of beta radiation as the equation shows:

$$^{130}_{52}\text{Te} + {}^{1}_{0}\text{n} \rightarrow {}^{131}_{52}\text{Te} \rightarrow {}^{131}_{53}\text{I} + {}^{0}_{-1}\beta$$

^{131}I has a half-life of about 8 days. It emits a beta-minus (β^-) particle and some gamma radiation:

$$^{131}_{53}\text{I} \rightarrow {}^{131}_{54}\text{Xe} + {}^{0}_{-1}\beta + \gamma$$

$^{99}_{42}$Mo, a widely used molybdenum radio-nuclide, is also produced by neutron bombardment. $^{99}_{42}$Mo has a half-life of 67 hours and decays to a nuclide of technetium:

$$^{99}_{42}\text{Mo} \rightarrow {}^{99\text{m}}_{43}\text{Tc} + {}^{0}_{-1}\beta$$

The 'm' in $^{99\text{m}}_{43}$Tc means that the technetium is *metastable*. The nucleus is in a higher energy state than normal. It decays down to stable $^{99}_{43}$Tc by emitting a gamma ray; the half-life for this decay is 6.0 hours. For the medical physicist, the important part of this decay is the emission of gamma radiation, which can be detected.

Elution

Figure M16 shows a $^{99\text{m}}_{43}$Tc generator, called an *elution cell*. The alumina column holds the chemicals. It contains a molybdenum compound, made with $^{99}_{42}$Mo. This decays continuously, producing a compound of $^{99\text{m}}_{43}$Tc. When the technetium is required, saline (salt) solution is passed through the alumina column and dissolves the technetium compound, but not the insoluble molybdenum. The eluted technetium solution is collected in the glass container.

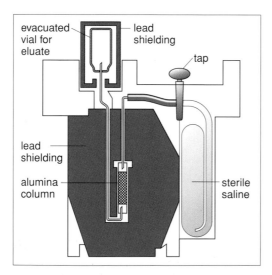

Figure M16 Saline solution, drawn through the alumina column by the vacuum in the vial, dissolves technetium

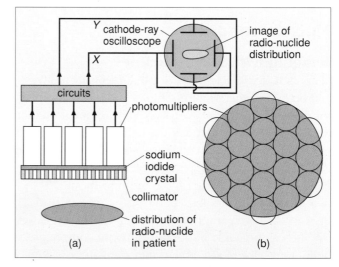

Figure M17 (a) Gamma radiation produces flashes of light in the crystal, which are amplified by photomultipliers and processed by the circuits. (b) Arrangement of photomultiplier tubes

The gamma camera

Gamma emissions from within the body are detected by a gamma camera (Figure M17). The gamma camera consists of four parts – a collimator, a sodium iodide scintillator, a set of photomultiplier tubes and a computer processor.

The collimator grid ensures that only gamma rays from directly in front of the camera strike the scintillator. When gamma rays pass through a sodium iodide crystal, flashes of light, called *scintillations*, are produced. These flashes of light land on the entrance windows of photomultiplier tubes. The light causes the phosphor at the entrance of the tube to emit electrons. These electrons are accelerated down the tube by a series of increasing positive voltages. As they hit the dynodes arranged along the tubes, they cause more electrons to be emitted. So a tiny flash of light produces a large pulse of current, which can be detected electronically.

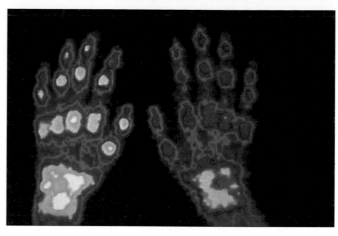

Figure M18 The bright spots on the hand on the left show the concentration of the radio-nuclide, produced by inflamed joints

The pulses of current from the set of photomultipliers are processed to produce an image showing the distribution of gamma emissions from the body.

Figure M18 shows a gamma camera image of hands with inflamed joints (arthritis). The hand on the left is severely arthritic, and the radio-nuclide has concentrated in the joints on this hand.

Radiological protection

Just as with X-rays, any exposure of the body to radioactive emissions has some risk attached. For this reason, radioactivity is only used when the possible benefits are greater than the risks. Those using radio-nuclides regularly protect themselves with lead shielding to minimise the doses they receive.

The radio-nuclides used on patients are chosen to have a half-life as short as possible, compatible with the time needed for the experiment. Pure gamma emitters are preferred to emitters of alpha and beta radiation, because the latter do not help imaging, but merely give an unnecessary dose of radiation to the body. For example, ^{123}I has replaced ^{131}I for testing thyroid function, as it is a pure gamma emitter.

On the other hand, patients with an over-active thyroid are given doses of ^{131}I so that the beta radiation emitted destroys part of the thyroid and reduces its activity.

Magnetic resonance imaging

Magnetic resonance imaging (MRI) is sometimes called nuclear magnetic resonance (NMR). It is a comparatively new technique for producing high-resolution images without radiation hazard. MRI relies on properties of the hydrogen nucleus. The single proton of the hydrogen nucleus spins and acts like a tiny bar magnet. When there is no external magnetic field, the individual nuclear magnetisms are randomly directed. In an MRI scanner (Figure M19), a huge magnetic field from the main coils causes the spin of each nucleus to precess

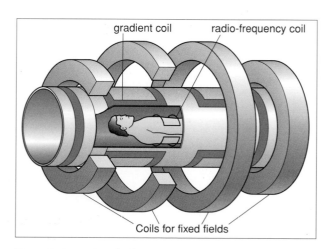

Figure M19 In MRI, the large coils produce a strong fixed magnetic field

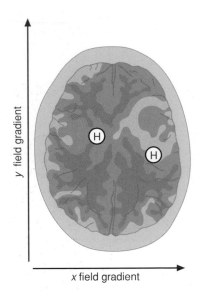

Figure M20 The variation of the magnetic field across the patient is known. So the scanner can locate the two hydrogen nuclei shown. The shading shows the density of hydrogen atoms across a brain with a tumour

(rotate) around the external field with a frequency that depends on the field strength. To produce large enough fields, the main coils are made from superconducting material, which needs to be kept within a few degrees of absolute zero by liquid helium coolant. At a typical field strength of 1.5 tesla (much stronger than the strongest laboratory magnet), the frequency of precession of the hydrogen nuclei is 64 MHz.

Smaller gradient coils produce a gradient in the magnetic field, so that the frequency of precession is different in each part of the patient. So from the precession frequency of a hydrogen nucleus and a knowledge of the field throughout the patient, the position of the nucleus can be found (Figure M20).

The radio-frequency coil produces pulses of electromagnetic radiation at the precession frequency and causes resonance. This gives the nuclei energy, which they emit after the pulse has stopped. The emitted radiations are received by an aerial and processed to produce an image.

The advantages of MRI

The power of an MRI scanner justifies its large cost, but the cost is such that scanners are used in shifts throughout the whole day and often the night as well. There are no risks of ionising radiation associated with MRI, and the resolution is amazingly good. Since it looks principally at hydrogen density, it can produce clear images of structures that are not apparent with other techniques, e.g. blood and brain, which cannot be clearly differentiated with X-rays or ultrasound. Figure M21 shows an MRI scan of a thorax.

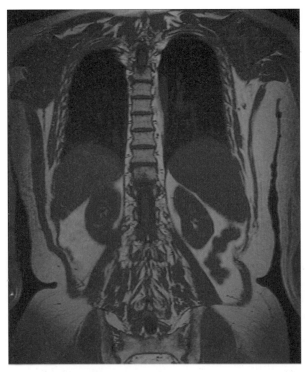

Figure M21 An MRI scan of a thorax

Astrophysics Topic

The birth of stars

Matter in space

Space is not a vacuum completely devoid of atoms. Between the stars there are large, irregular *gas clouds* (Figure A1) containing only a few atoms of hydrogen, helium and cosmic dust per cubic centimetre. An interstellar gas cloud can contract under the pull of its own gravitational forces. As the atoms get closer, their gravitational potential energy decreases and their kinetic energy increases. You saw in Chapter 8 that temperature is proportional to the mean kinetic energy of the atoms. Thus, as the atoms get closer their temperature increases. Initially, however, the gas cloud remains fairly cool, because energy travels to its surface, by convection, and then radiates out into space.

Figure A1 Stars are born within such a gas cloud; this one is in the Orion nebula

As the interstellar gas cloud contracts more, its increasing density makes it more difficult for internal energy to reach the surface by convection and the denser regions warm up. If a cloud's mass is large (at least 100 times that of our Sun), the temperature rise of the high-density regions is sufficient to allow nuclear fusion to take place. The cloud then fragments into regions with high central temperatures, each of which forms a star. Fusion takes place only within the core of a star. About 10% of the mass is involved in fusion. This 10% of mass is a much smaller proportion of the volume, because the core is denser.

Relatively small interstellar gas clouds do not ever reach high enough temperatures for nuclear fusion. These *brown dwarfs* just become hot enough to emit infra-red radiation.

The fusion process

Hydrogen nuclei (protons, $_1^1$H) need energy to bring them together against the large electrostatic repulsive forces. But when they approach to within about 10^{-13} m, they join together and give out much more energy as strong nuclear forces bind them together. This energy raises their random kinetic energy: they get hotter.

The electrostatic potential energy of two protons (each of charge $q = 1.6 \times 10^{-19}$ C) at fusion separation r is

$$W = [1/(4\pi\varepsilon_0)]q^2/r$$
$$= [9 \times 10^9 \, \mathrm{J\,m\,C^{-2}}] \times (1.6 \times 10^{-19}\,\mathrm{C})^2/(1.0 \times 10^{-13}\,\mathrm{m})$$
$$= 2.3 \times 10^{-15}\,\mathrm{J}$$

Thus, a proton requires 2.3×10^{-15} J of kinetic energy to get close enough to allow fusion to occur. At what temperature will a proton have this kinetic energy?

ASTROPHYSICS TOPIC

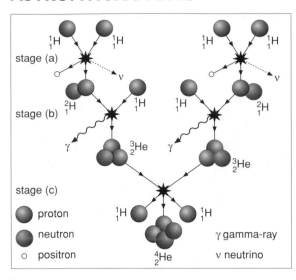

Figure A2 Proton–proton chain

In Chapter 8 we saw that $W = 3kT/2$. Hence

$T = 2W/3k$

$= (2 \times 2.3 \times 10^{-15}\,\text{J})/(3 \times 1.38 \times 10^{-23}\,\text{J}\,\text{K}^{-1})$

$= 1 \times 10^8\,\text{K} = 100\,000\,000\,\text{K}$

These extremely high temperatures are required for nuclear fusion to occur.

The fusion process, in which hydrogen nuclei become helium nuclei, is known as the *proton–proton (p–p) chain*. The p–p chain involves the emission of positrons (β^+), neutrinos (v) and gamma rays (γ), as shown in Figure A2. You can read more about the particles involved in the Particle Physics Topic in *Fields*.

The p–p chain consists of three stages:

$${}^{1}_{1}\text{H} + {}^{1}_{1}\text{H} \rightarrow {}^{2}_{1}\text{H} + {}^{0}_{1}\beta^+ + v \qquad \text{(a)}$$

$${}^{2}_{1}\text{H} + {}^{1}_{1}\text{H} \rightarrow {}^{3}_{2}\text{He} + \gamma \qquad \text{(b)}$$

$${}^{3}_{2}\text{He} + {}^{3}_{2}\text{He} \rightarrow {}^{4}_{2}\text{He} + 2{}^{1}_{1}\text{H} \qquad \text{(c)}$$

The whole fusion reaction can be represented by the equation:

$$4{}^{1}_{1}\text{H} \rightarrow {}^{4}_{2}\text{He} + 2{}^{0}_{1}\beta^+ + 2v + \text{energy}$$

Energy is released as gamma photons and kinetic energy of the resulting particles. Table A1 gives the masses of the particles involved in the fusion reaction.

Table A1 *Masses of particles involved in the proton–proton chain where $1\,u = 1.66 \times 10^{-27}\,kg$*

Particle		Mass/u
proton	${}^{1}_{1}\text{H}$	1.007 49
helium nucleus	${}^{4}_{2}\text{He}$	4.002 55
positron	${}^{0}_{1}\beta^+$	0.000 55
neutrino	v	negligible

How can we apply these numbers to the Sun? When each helium nucleus is formed, four protons, of total mass 4.029 96 u, become a particle of total mass 4.002 55 u. When the positions are taken into account the difference in mass is 0.026 31 u, which is $4.367\,46 \times 10^{-29}\,\text{kg}$. Using Einstein's famous equation $E = mc^2$, this mass is equivalent to $3.93 \times 10^{-12}\,\text{J}$ of energy released. (You can see how to do this calculation in Chapter 9 of *Matter and Waves*.) Although each fusion reaction releases only this small amount of energy, the very large number of reactions taking place each second in a star results in a very large rate of energy release, e.g. $3.8 \times 10^{26}\,\text{W}$ for the Sun. How many fusion reactions occur in the Sun each second? What is the mass of the energy released per second by the Sun?

Stable stars

Gravitational forces cause the star to contract and hydrogen fusion to start. Fusion within the core of a star increases internal temperature and pressure. The rate of fusion increases until the internal pressure is sufficient to prevent further gravitational collapse, as shown in Figure A3.

Gravitational forces are larger for more massive stars. So the rate of fusion increases further until internal pressure prevents further collapse. Consequently, more massive stars are hotter and brighter but use up their supply of hydrogen quicker.

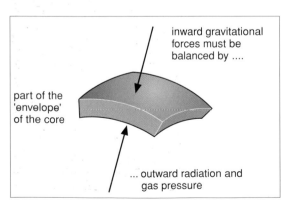

Figure A3 Fusion in the core of a star counteracts gravitational collapse

A star remains in this stable state until insufficient hydrogen is left in the core to allow fusion to continue. This stage is reached when only about 4% of the star's hydrogen has been used up. The Sun's mass is about 10^{30}kg. Its stable lifetime is estimated to be about 10^{10} years.

Energy transfer in stars

High-energy photons, created in the core, are continually absorbed by nuclei in the star and re-emitted as lower-energy photons. Photons only travel a few millimetres between each re-absorption and can be re-emitted in any direction, often back towards the core. This produces pressure, called *radiation pressure*.

Further away from the core the gas is cooler and more opaque to the radiation process. Beyond three-quarters of the radius, convection takes over as the main method of energy transfer. Hot gases rise, release their energy and sink. Transfer of energy through the star is a slow process, so the star stays hot for millions of years! The energy transfer processes are summarised in Figure A4.

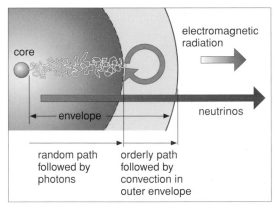

Figure A4 Energy transfer from core to space

Information from stars

Observing stars

The stars were first observed with the naked eye. Next came simple refracting telescopes and the more complicated reflecting telescopes. All three devices detect visible light from stars. This light has passed through the Earth's atmosphere and has been affected by it. For instance, continual local changes in atmospheric density cause stars to twinkle. The atmosphere, including the dust within it, absorbs and scatters more than 30% of the visible light incident on the Earth. Different wavelengths are absorbed by differing amounts, further distorting the information we receive.

As well as light, the various types of modern telescopes also detect infra-red and ultra-violet radiations, which suffer even more from atmospheric absorption. The best solution to get an undistorted view of the stars is to place the telescope in orbit above the Earth's atmosphere.

The Infrared Astronomical Satellite (IRAS), sent into orbit in 1983, created a detailed far-infra-red map of our view of the universe. In the early 1990s, the Cosmic Background Explorer (COBE) detected small ripples in the microwave background radiation reaching the Earth. The Hubble Space Telescope (Figure A5) continues to produce some stunning pictures (Figure A6).

Radio waves, having wavelengths from a few centimetres to 10 m, pass unaffected through our atmosphere. So there is no disadvantage having radio telescopes on the ground. Radio telescopes can be very large to help them detect and locate very weak radio signals. The largest radio telescope has a diameter of 300 m, but they can effectively be made much bigger by combining signals from several aerials many kilometres apart.

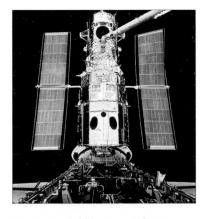

Figure A5 Hubble Space Telescope seen from the Space Shuttle

Figure A6 The Cygnus Loop supernova remnant as seen from the Hubble Space Telescope

Black-body radiation and surface temperature

Bodies in space both absorb and emit electromagnetic radiation. Black surfaces are perfect absorbers. They appear black because they absorb all the radiation falling on them. Black surfaces are also perfect emitters.

Figure A7 shows the energy distribution of the radiation emitted from a black body at different temperatures. The graph shows that a hot black body emits a wide range of wavelengths. The wavelength at which the intensity peaks (λ_{max}) decreases with increasing temperature. Wien's law states that λ_{max} is inversely proportional to the Kelvin temperature T of the black body. Thus

$$\lambda_{max} \propto 1/T$$

and so

$$\lambda_{max}T = \text{a constant} = 2.898 \times 10^{-3}\,\text{m K}$$

The peak wavelengths on the graph lie in the infra-red, although the body at 1400 K emits a small amount of visible light and appears 'red hot'. A hotter body emitting all visible wavelengths will appear 'white hot'.

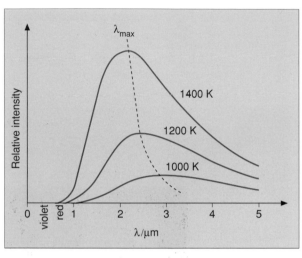

Figure A7 Black-body energy distribution

You can regard stars as being perfect emitters, and therefore black bodies. You can calculate the surface temperature of a star from its observed λ_{max} value. Astronomical objects whose intensity peaks at X-ray wavelengths are at extremely high temperatures (10^7 K), while those peaking at radio wavelengths are close to absolute zero.

Luminosity of a star

Luminosity L is the total power emitted over all wavelengths. The area under each of the curves in Figure A7 gives the luminosity per unit area at the surface for a black body at that temperature. Obviously, luminosity increases with temperature. The *Stefan–Boltzmann law* states that the luminosity of a black body is proportional to the fourth power of its Kelvin temperature. A body's surface area A also determines its luminosity. Thus

$$L = \sigma T^4 A$$

where Stefan's constant $\sigma = 5.67 \times 10^{-8}\,\text{W m}^{-2}\text{K}^{-4}$.

For a spherical star of radius r behaving like a black body, $A = 4\pi r^2$. So

$$L = 4\pi r^2 \sigma T^4$$

Using this we find that the luminosity of the Sun (radius 7.0×10^8 m and surface temperature 5800 K) is 3.9×10^{26} W.

Intensity

The *flux density or intensity* of a star is the power per metre squared from it that arrives on the Earth. Intensity F depends on luminosity L and also the distance D of the star from the Earth:

$$F = L/(4\pi D^2)$$

A distant star will have a lower intensity than a close star of the same luminosity. The intensity of a star can be measured. If its distance from the Earth is known, you can calculate its luminosity.

Measuring astronomical distances

Astronomical distances are so great that special units are used. Two of these are shown in Table A2.

Table A2 *Two units used for astronomical distances*

Unit	Definition	Metre equivalent
Astronomical unit (AU)	Average distance between Earth and Sun	$1\,\text{AU} = 1.496 \times 10^{11}\,\text{m}$
Light year (ly)	Distance travelled by light in one year	$1\,\text{ly} = 9.46 \times 10^{15}\,\text{m}$

The distance to a nearby star is measured using *annual parallax*. The star's position is recorded against the static background of more distant stars when the Earth is at opposite extremes of its orbit around the Sun. The parallax angle p (Figure A8) is measured and then the distance D is calculated from

$$D = 1\,\text{AU}/\tan p$$

Even the closest star is very far away, and the angle p is extremely small. This angle gets even smaller for more distant stars. Parallax angles down to $1/360\,000°$ can be measured, making this method suitable for measuring star distances up to $10^{18}\,\text{m}$.

The Hertzsprung–Russell diagram

You can find the temperature of a star from the wavelength of maximum intensity, using Wien's law. From measurements of intensity and distance, you can also calculate the luminosity of that star. If you then plot luminosity against decreasing temperature for a large number of stars, you get a graph like that shown in Figure A9. Each dot on the graph represents at least one star. This graph is called the Hertzsprung–Russell (H-R) diagram. Note that its temperature scale *decreases* to the right.

Figure A8 $D = 1\,\text{AU}/\tan p$

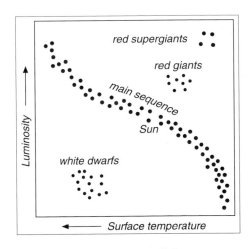

Figure A9 *Hertzsprung–Russell diagram*

The star plots on the H-R diagram form a distinct pattern, a curve from top left to bottom right through the centre of the diagram. This pattern involves a wide variety of stars: from extremely massive, luminous blue stars (top left) to extremely dim and less-massive red stars (bottom right). A star remains in the same position on this graph for the whole of the period whilst its core is undergoing hydrogen fusion, about 90% of its total lifetime. This pattern is called the *main sequence*.

Figure A9 shows two groups of stars above and towards the right of the main sequence. These are cool (red) stars with a high luminosity. For a low-temperature star to emit this much power, it must have a very large surface area. Hence they are known as *red giants* and *red supergiants*.

Another group of stars is shown below and towards the left of the main sequence. These are hot (white) stars with a low luminosity. For a high-temperature star to emit so little power, it must have a very small surface area. Hence they are known as *white dwarfs*. All three groups consist of stars that have completed their core-hydrogen fusion and left the main sequence. You will find more about these later in this Topic.

Measuring greater distances

Astronomers can use parallax to find the distance of close stars only. For distant stars, they use the H-R diagram. First, they measure the temperature, as for any star, using Wien's law. Then they use the H-R diagram to predict the luminosity L. Finally, they measure the intensity F. Then, using the formula $F = L/(4\pi D^2)$, they calculate the distance D.

There is a type of star called a *Cepheid variable*. For these stars, their brightness varies with a period that depends on their luminosity. If astronomers measure the period of a distant Cepheid variable, they can find the luminosity, and hence can calculate their distance from the Earth.

Star spectra

Chapter 29 of *Matter and Waves* shows how to use a diffraction grating to observe the line emission spectra of various elements. You can use a grating to analyse light from individual stars and compare this with light from known elements.

Sometimes certain frequencies are missing from a spectrum. This can be equally revealing. For instance, sunlight does not produce a continuous visible spectrum but one with some dark lines across it. Two of these occur in the yellow and denote the absorption of these two frequencies by sodium in the Sun's atmosphere. Not surprisingly, the presence of absorption lines also confirms that the majority of star matter consists of hydrogen and helium.

Star movements

The spectra of many stars display a displaced pattern, with all the dark lines occurring at lower frequencies than they should. The lines are displaced towards the longer-wavelength (red) end of the spectrum. *Red-shift* occurs as a result of the source of light moving away from the observer. If the source of light is moving towards the observer, frequency increases, wavelength decreases and blue-shift occurs. This phenomenon is the *Doppler effect*. The change in both frequency Δf and wavelength $\Delta\lambda$ is related to the speed v at which the star is moving by the following equation:

$$\Delta f/f = \Delta\lambda/\lambda = v/c$$

where c is the speed of light.

The fact that light from the majority of galaxies exhibits a red-shift is evidence for an expanding universe.

Hubble's law

Using red-shift data, the recession velocity of a large number of galaxies can be found. Edwin Hubble discovered that the recession velocity is directly proportional to the galaxy's distance from us.

The equation of the line in Figure A10 relates the recession velocity v to the distance D:

$$v = HD$$

where H is the *Hubble constant*. Unfortunately, the value of the Hubble constant is rather uncertain, reflecting the uncertainty in the measurements of astronomical distances. Its value is $(2 \pm 1) \times 10^{-18}\,\text{s}^{-1}$.

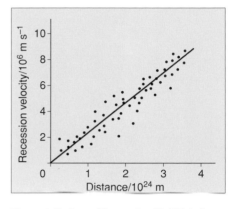

Figure A10 Data illustrating Hubble's law

Assuming that all galaxies are moving away from the same starting point (the Big Bang) and that their individual speeds have not varied, we get:

age of universe = (distance travelled)/speed

$$= D/v = D/HD = 1/H$$

Using the above value for H, we obtain

age of universe $= 1/(2 \times 10^{-18}\,\text{s}^{-1}) = 5 \times 10^{17}\,\text{s} \approx 10^{10}\,\text{years}$

Binary stars

A binary pair consists of two stars orbiting around their common centre of mass, with the more massive star of the pair having the smallest orbit (Figure A11). If they are passing in front of each other as we see them, we can measure the variable intensity that results.

The total mass M of two binary stars having a separation r is given by:

$$M = 4\pi^2 r^3/GT^2$$

where T is the period of rotation and G is the universal gravitational constant ($6.67 \times 10^{-11}\,\text{N}\,\text{m}^2\,\text{kg}^{-2}$). Mass M is equal to the sum of the masses of the two binary stars, i.e. $M = M_1 + M_2$. Their separation r is the sum of their distances from the common centre of mass, i.e. $r = R_1 + R_2$. The ratio of the masses of the stars is in the inverse ratio of the distances from the common centre of mass (Figure A11):

$$M_1/M_2 = R_2/R_1$$

Binary stars provide one of the very few practical ways of estimating a star's mass. This has been done for several hundred binary stars, although there are still many others out there waiting to be massed!

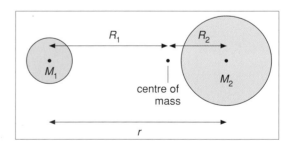

Figure A11 A binary pair of stars; $M_1/M_2 = R_2/R_1$

The death of stars

Life after the main sequence

Nuclear processes in the core of a main-sequence star stop once there is insufficient hydrogen there for fusion. The core temperature is too low for fusion of helium nuclei to occur immediately. An envelope of unburnt hydrogen remains outside the core.

As fusion stops in the core, gravitational forces again become dominant and the core contracts, causing the star's temperature to increase. Fusion of the hydrogen now occurs in a shell around the core. The region of fusion is now further out, and so constrained by less matter outside it. There is sufficient energy released to cause the outer envelope of the star to expand around its still shrinking core. The star's diameter increases by a factor of about 100 during this stage of the process and a red giant is formed.

The more massive the star, the greater its ultimate core temperature. The core temperature may reach a point where helium fusion occurs, leading to the formation of beryllium and carbon. Both reactions release energy and raise the temperature of the core:

$$_{2}^{4}\text{He} \ + \ _{2}^{4}\text{He} \ \rightarrow \ _{4}^{8}\text{Be} \ + \ \text{energy}$$

$$_{4}^{8}\text{Be} \ + \ _{2}^{4}\text{He} \ \rightarrow \ _{6}^{12}\text{C} \ + \ \text{energy}$$

As the mass of the core increases, the temperature gets higher. This causes larger nuclei to fuse and create even heavier elements. This process takes place progressively, in shells. So as one fusion process ends, the next process begins, but only when the shell has heated up even more. The most massive stars are capable of forming an iron core surrounded by layers supporting different fusion processes, as shown in Figure A12. If the Sun became a red supergiant, it would engulf almost all the space out to the orbit of Jupiter. The elements in the cores of lower-mass stars are of an intermediate mass.

Large amounts of matter are ejected from the distant outer envelope of a red giant where the gravitational field is weaker. A red giant loses mass ten million times faster than the Sun.

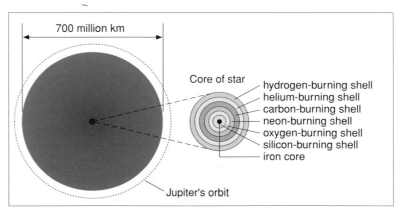

Figure A12 Fusion layers within a red supergiant

The end of the road

At some point, the energy available from further gravitational collapse is insufficient to trigger the next fusion stage. Indeed, as you can read in Chapter 9 of *Matter and Waves*, any further fusion after the production of iron takes in energy as it occurs, causing the star to cool and shrink. The layers outside the core continue fusion for some time. The inactive core region grows until the elements in the outer layers are of the same mass as those within the core. Effectively, the fire goes out and gravitational forces finally succeed in collapsing the star. There are a number of end games that a star can play, the one followed depending entirely on the star's original mass.

Low-mass stars

Fusion eventually stops. The remnant of a red giant cools down and shrinks. As it contracts, its gravitational potential energy decreases and the star becomes very hot. This small, and very hot, star is a *white dwarf*.

The electrons in the core are forced into a smaller and smaller volume, and there comes a limit, smaller than which they will not go. The electrons are then said to be *degenerate*. The *electron degeneracy pressure* resists any further inward collapse.

A white dwarf of similar size to the Earth would have a mass of about 10^{30} kg. Comparing this with that of the Earth (mass 6×10^{24} kg) shows that the average density of a white dwarf is much greater. Its nuclei and electrons must be much closer than in the atomic arrangements found on Earth.

High-mass stars

The fate of red supergiants with original masses greater than eight times that of the Sun is very spectacular. They have sufficient mass to overcome electron degeneracy pressure. The electrons combine with protons to form neutrons. A rapid collapse of the massive degenerate iron core then takes place. A large amount of gravitational potential energy is released during this implosion and is sufficient to promote fusion of elements heavier than iron. These, together with all the star's outer layers, are then blown away into interstellar space by the resulting shock wave, and a very bright *supernova* is formed.

The central core of neutrons left behind is most likely to form a *neutron star*. These are extremely dense objects. They are like a giant nucleus. Typically, they will contain a mass of about 10^{30} kg within a diameter of 20 km, giving a density about 10^{15} times greater than normal matter.

With such small surface areas, neutron stars emit insufficient thermal radiation for detection by normal visual or thermal telescopes. However, since they are both magnetised and rotating, they continually emit a high-frequency radio signal along their magnetic axis (Figure A13).

*Figure A13 Rotating
neutron stars
produce pulsars*

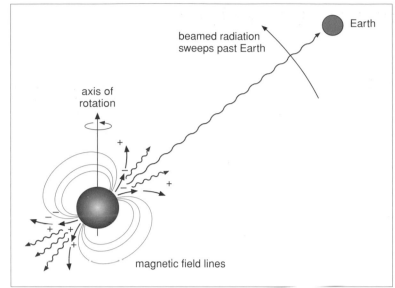

This signal sweeps across space as the neutron star rotates, in a similar way to the beam of light issuing from a lighthouse. A pulse of radio waves is detected each time the beam sweeps past the Earth. *Pulsars* were first detected in 1967. Their connection with neutron stars and supernovae was established a year later when a pulsar was found at the centre of the Crab nebula (Figure A14). The supernova from which this was formed was recorded by Chinese astronomers in 1054.

*Figure A14 The Crab
nebula has a pulsar
at its centre*

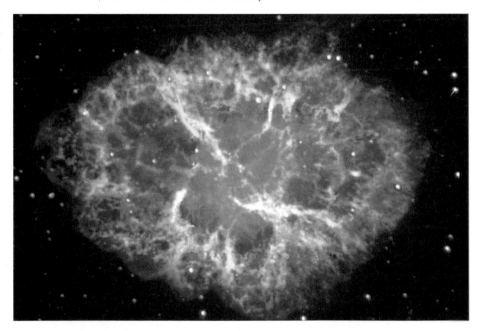

If the neutron core is greater than three solar masses, gravitational attraction is strong enough to shrink the core until it is no more than a point, referred to as a singularity. A black hole is a region of space, surrounding a singularity, from within which no light, matter or signal of any kind can achieve the required velocity to escape. Despite this, detection is still possible where a black hole is one of a binary system. Material sucked from the companion star becomes extremely hot and emits X-rays as it falls into the black hole. Strong X-ray sources, associated with a single star, indicate the presence of a companion black hole.

Practice questions

Chapter 1

1.1 Describe the experiment that you would use to calibrate a liquid-in-glass thermometer. The alcohol level in an uncalibrated alcohol-in-glass thermometer is 2.0 cm above its bulb when the thermometer is placed in melting ice, and 18.0 cm above its bulb when in pure, boiling water at atmospheric pressure. Calculate how far the alcohol level will be from the bulb when the thermometer is at a temperature of: (a) 35°C and (b) –8°C.

1.2 A thermocouple is connected across a very sensitive ammeter that has a resistance of 16 Ω. One junction of the thermocouple is maintained at 0 °C and the other at 160 °C. The e.m.f. that this thermocouple generates is $35\,\mu V\,°C^{-1}$ of the temperature difference between its two junctions. If the thermocouple has a resistance of 4 Ω, calculate (a) the current flowing through the galvanometer and (b) the power produced by the thermocouple. State two advantages and one disadvantage that a thermocouple has compared with a liquid-in-glass thermometer.

1.3 What is meant when two bodies are said to be in *thermal equilibrium*? Is thermal equilibrium a dynamic or static situation? Explain your answer.

Chapter 2

2.1 State *Boyle's law*. Describe how you would test this law in the laboratory. Your answer should include a diagram of the apparatus and refer to any precautions that you would take. How would you use your readings to show that the law is valid?

2.2 A gas cylinder, volume 0.06 m³, contains air at a pressure of 1.8 MPa. The tap of the cylinder is opened and the air escapes into the atmosphere. Given that atmospheric pressure is 100 kPa, calculate the volume of air (measured at atmospheric pressure) that leaves the cylinder.

2.3 A fish resting on the bottom of a lake releases a small air bubble from its mouth and watches it rise up towards the surface. The bubble increases in volume as it journeys to the surface through water that is known to be at a constant temperature. (a) Explain why the volume of the bubble increases as it rises to the surface. (b) The volume of the released bubble was 4 mm³ but this had increased to 20 mm³ by the time that it had reached the surface. Given that the atmospheric pressure acting on the surface of the lake is equivalent to an additional 10 m of water, calculate the depth of the lake at the point where the fish is resting. Explain all your working.

Chapter 3

3.1 State the *pressure law*. The following set of corresponding readings of temperature and pressure were recorded.

Temperature/°C	1	12	29	34	58	78
Pressure/kPa	96	100	106	111	116	123

Unfortunately, one of the temperature readings has been written down incorrectly. Find out which one. Use all the other data to determine the correct value for this temperature. Show all your working.

3.2 A flask has its cork inserted when the air pressure is equivalent to a column of mercury that is 750 mm high [written as 750 mmHg] and the temperature is 15°C. The temperature of the flask is then gradually increased. The cork blows out of the neck of the flask when the pressure of the air inside it exceeds atmospheric pressure by 150 mmHg. Calculate the temperature, in °C, at which this will happen.

3.3 A fixed mass of gas has an initial volume V_0 and an initial pressure p_0. It is first compressed at a constant temperature of 27 °C until its volume is reduced to $\frac{1}{4}V_0$. State the pressure of the gas, in terms of p_0, at the end of this process. The temperature of the gas is now increased until its volume returns to its original value. Throughout this process, the gas is allowed to expand in such a way that its pressure remains constant. Calculate the final temperature, in °C, of the gas. Illustrate these two changes on a graph of pressure against volume. Describe the third change that is required to complete the 'cycle' of changes, i.e. to return the gas to its original conditions.

Chapter 4

4.1 Derive the equation for the pressure at the bottom of a column of liquid of height h and density ρ. On a certain day, a barometer reading gives the atmospheric pressure as being equivalent to a column of mercury that has a vertical height of 77 cm. Calculate the atmospheric pressure in pascals (the density of mercury is 13 600 kg m^{-3}). Assuming that the density of air throughout the atmosphere is 1.25 kg m^{-3}, calculate an approximate value for the height of the atmosphere. State and explain how your calculated value compares with the accepted value for the height of the atmosphere.

4.2 On a certain day, the reading of a mercury barometer is 75.58 cm at sea-level and 66.37 cm on the summit of a nearby mountain. Use the density values given in the previous question to estimate the height of the mountain.

4.3 Describe the experiment that you would use to find the density of air.

Chapter 5

5.1 State *Archimedes' principle*. A woman, of mass 70 kg, is floating in water. Calculate the upthrust on her. The density of water is 1000 kg m^{-3}. Calculate the volume of water she displaces.

5.2 A fisherman catches a fish of mass 3 kg. The tension on the line is 6 N while the fish is in the water.

(a) Calculate the upthrust on the fish and draw a free-body force diagram for the fish. (b) Calculate the volume of water displaced by the fish and the density of the fish. (c) Calculate the tension in the line when the fish is out of the water.

5.3 A buoy of mass 50 kg floats with half of its volume out of water. Calculate the volume of the float. The float is tied to the sea bed with a short chain and gets pulled under the water when the tide rises. Draw a free-body diagram for this situation and calculate the tension in the chain.

Chapter 6

6.1 Draw a free-body diagram for an aircraft in level flight. The velocity of the aircraft is constant. Explain what you can about the forces on it.

6.2 Draw a free-body diagram for an aircraft climbing at 30° to the horizontal at a constant velocity. Explain what you can about the forces on it.

6.3 Explain why vehicle designers use sleek shapes for cars, but not for fork-lift trucks.

Chapter 7

7.1 Describe an experimental arrangement for observing the Brownian motion of smoke particles suspended in air. State what is observed and explain how the observations support the view that a gas consists of particles in rapid, random motion.

7.2 A ball bearing model of a gas attempts to model gas properties in terms of the random motion of its particles. Explain *qualitatively* how this theory accounts for: (a) the pressure exerted by a gas on the walls of its container; (b) the relationship between pressure and volume of a fixed mass of gas maintained at a constant temperature; and (c) the relationship between pressure and temperature of a fixed mass of gas maintained at a constant volume.

Chapter 8

8.1   A steady stream of balls, each of mass 0.2 kg, hits a vertical wall at right angles. The speed of the balls is $15\,\text{ms}^{-1}$ and 600 hit the wall in 12 s. Assuming that the balls rebound at the same speed, calculate the average force acting on the wall during this period of time. *Sketch* a graph to show how the actual force on the wall varies with time over a period of 100 ms. You should assume that the force changes in a linear way during each individual collision. Explain how the average force acting on the wall can be obtained from your graph.

8.2   The pressure exerted by an ideal gas can be written in the form $p = \frac{1}{3}\rho\langle c^2\rangle$ where the symbols have their usual meanings. What does each symbol represent? Show that the equation is *homogeneous* with respect to its units. State four of the assumptions that are made about an ideal gas when deriving this equation.

8.3   The density of hydrogen gas at a pressure of 101 kPa and a temperature of 0 °C is $90\,\text{gm}^{-3}$. Calculate the root mean square speed of its molecules under these conditions. Sketch a graph showing the distribution of the speeds of the hydrogen molecules. On the same axes, sketch the new distribution for the same gas at a higher temperature.

8.4   The mean (translational) kinetic energy of a gas molecule is given by the equation $\frac{1}{2}mv^2 = 3kT/2$ where k is the gas constant per molecule, known as the *Boltzmann constant* $(1.38 \times 10^{-23}\,\text{JK}^{-1})$. (a) Show that the equation is homogeneous with respect to its units. (b) State the relationship between the Boltzmann, the Avogadro and the molar gas constants. (c) The root mean square speed of the molecules of a gas is known

to be $380\,\text{ms}^{-1}$ at a temperature of 7 °C. Calculate their root mean square speed at a temperature of 847 °C.

8.5   Eight gas molecules are moving along the same line with the following velocities (measured in ms^{-1}): 350, 420, −280, 610, −680, −540, 590, −490. Calculate: (a) the mean speed of these molecules, (b) the mean velocity, (c) the mean square velocity, and (d) the root mean square speed.

Chapter 9

9.1   Describe the motion of the molecules in a solid, a liquid and a gas. For each state, explain how the substance can store internal energy.

9.2   A hot body is placed next to a cold body. Explain why there is a net flow from hot to cold if energy moves randomly between the two bodies.

9.3   Two bodies are in *thermal equilibrium*. What can you say about their internal energy?

9.4   Compare the internal energies and the temperatures of a spoonful of hot water and a bucketful of cold water.

Chapter 10

10.1   Good electrical conductors such as copper are also good thermal conductors, although the reverse is not always correct. For instance, quartz is a good conductor of heat but a very poor conductor of electricity. These statements support the fact that two possible mechanisms exist by which heat can be conducted through a solid. Describe these two mechanisms with reference to both copper and quartz.

10.2 Explain how energy gets from the flame of a gas cooker to the whole contents of a pan of water above the flame.

10.3 For each of conduction, convection, radiation and evaporation, describe one situation in which they are helpful, and one situation in which they are unhelpful.

Chapter 11

11.1 Define *thermal conductivity*. Express the units of thermal conductivity in terms of only base units. The thermal conductivity of brick is $0.6\,Wm^{-1}K^{-1}$. A brick wall has a thickness of 10cm and an area of $12\,m^2$. Calculate the rate of heat flow through the wall when the temperature difference across its surfaces is 15K.

11.2 Sketch the pattern of the heat flow through a perfectly lagged metal bar. Explain why the temperature gradient is uniform along its length. A uniform, perfectly lagged metal bar has thermal energy flowing through it. The temperature is 80°C at 8.0cm from the hot end and 50°C at 20cm from the same end. Calculate the temperature gradient along the metal bar. How far from the hot end will the temperature be 60°C? The 'cold' end of the metal bar is being maintained at a constant temperature of 30°C. What is the length of the bar?

11.3 The following temperatures were recorded at various positions along an unlagged metal bar whose hot end was being maintained at a temperature of 100°C:

Distance from hot end/cm	0	2	4	6	8	10	12	14
Temperature/°C	100	76	58	44	35	28	24	21

Plot a graph of temperature against distance from the hot end of the metal bar. Use your graph to find the temperature gradient at a distance of 5cm from the hot end of the metal bar.

11.4 Define the term *U-value*. Explain why architects and builders prefer to use *U-values* rather than thermal conductivities. The *U-value* of a well-insulated roof is $0.4\,Wm^{-2}K^{-1}$. Calculate the energy lost per minute through such a roof of area $50\,m^2$ when it has a temperature difference of 14°C across it.

Chapter 12

12.1 Define the heat capacity of a body. Express the units of heat capacity in terms of only base units. A thermally insulated coil of wire of resistance 25Ω and heat capacity $12\,JK^{-1}$ has a potential difference of 5.0V applied across its ends. Calculate the temperature rise produced in one minute.

12.2 Describe the experiment that you would use to determine the *specific heat capacity* of a metal block by an electrical heating method. Your answer should include a circuit diagram and refer to any precautions that you would take when performing the experiment. Explain how the specific heat capacity of the metal is calculated from your results.

12.3 A 5.0kg block of copper is heated for 8min by an electric heater of heat capacity $300\,JK^{-1}$ embedded in it. The potential difference across the heater is 25V and it carries a current of 2A. The temperature of the block increases by 10K. Calculate the specific heat capacity of copper.

12.4 The braking system on each of the four wheels of a car consists of a metal disc attached to the wheel and a pad attached to the framework of the car. During braking the pads grip the discs so that the car slows down. Each disc has a mass of 2.8kg and its metal has a specific heat capacity of $460\,Jkg^{-1}K^{-1}$. Calculate: (a) the heat capacity of a single disc and (b) an approximate value for the temperature rise of each disc when the car of mass

900kg brakes from a speed of 30ms⁻¹ to rest. (c) A single disc is removed from the car. An experiment involving 'the method of mixtures' is used to check the value of its specific heat capacity. Describe this experiment.

Chapter 13

13.1   Describe the experiment that you would use to determine the *specific latent heat of fusion* of water by an electrical heating method. Your answer should include a circuit diagram and refer to any precautions that you would take when performing the experiment. Explain how the specific latent heat of fusion of water is calculated from your results.

13.2   The *specific latent heat of vaporisation* of water is 2.25 MJ kg⁻¹. Calculate the amount of energy required to turn 16g of boiling water into steam. An electric heater decreases the mass of boiling water in an insulated container by 16g in 1min. What is the minimum power of this heater? Why is the actual power likely to be greater? The potential difference across the heater and the current flowing through it are 230V and 3.2A respectively. Calculate the efficiency with which the heater is changing water into steam.

13.3   An automatic electric kettle of heat capacity 350J K⁻¹ operates at a potential difference of 230V and a current of 8A. It is used to heat 600g of water (specific heat capacity = 4.2 kJ kg⁻¹K⁻¹) and itself from an initial temperature of 15°C. Assuming that there are no energy losses and no evaporation takes place, calculate the time taken to bring the water to the boil. The automatic cut-off fails to function. The kettle is manually turned off two minutes after the water began to boil. How much water will be left in the kettle?

13.4   A certain variety of carrots has a specific heat capacity of 3700J kg⁻¹K⁻¹. A saucepan of boiling water is used to raise the temperature of 825g of these carrots to 100°C. The carrots are then *quickly* drained and *immediately* transferred to a large amount of ice and water in a plastic bowl (a process known as *blanching*). It is noticed that some of the ice still remains when the carrots achieve thermal equilibrium with the ice/water mixture. Given that the specific latent heat of fusion of water is 330kJ kg⁻¹, calculate the mass of ice that melts during this process. Discuss the effect on the amount of ice that melts of using a metal bucket instead of a plastic bowl. You should consider the situation (a) immediately after the carrots have been added and (b) towards the end of the blanching process.

13.5   Three kilograms of molten lead at an initial temperature of 608K are allowed to cool down. The temperature takes 16s to decrease to 600K and then remains at this value for 5min. It then decreases by a further 6K in the next 10s. The rate at which the lead loses energy to its surroundings can be taken to be uniform throughout this period as its temperature remains fairly constant. *Sketch* a temperature–time graph for the above and state what has happened to the lead during this period of time. The specific heat capacity of lead when in its solid form is 130J kg⁻¹K⁻¹. Find: (a) the rate of loss of energy from the lead, (b) the specific latent heat of fusion of lead and (c) the specific heat capacity of lead when in its liquid form.

Chapter 14

14.1   A cold cell can transfer energy to a hot lamp filament. Explain why the process must be *working* not *heating*.

14.2   Calculate the kinetic energy of a hammer head, of mass 0.3kg, travelling at 15ms⁻¹. Fifty such blows of the hammer are landed upon a piece of lead of mass 0.15kg. At the end the lead is hot, and the hammer is still cold. Explain how the hammer can raise the temperature of the block without heating it. Calculate the energy transferred to the lead block and its temperature rise, given that the specific heat capacity of lead is $130 \, \mathrm{J \, kg^{-1} K^{-1}}$.

14.3 Explain why the electric mains supply *works* on an electric fire rather than *heats* it. How does the energy then get from the fire to the room?

Chapter 15

15.1 Show that the product $p\Delta V$ has the same units as work. A chemical reaction expands a gas syringe by 0.25 litres when the surrounding atmospheric pressure is 101 kPa. Calculate the work done.

15.2 The first law of thermodynamics can be stated in the form of the equation $\Delta Q + \Delta W = \Delta U$. Explain carefully the meaning of each of the terms in this equation. What important principle of physics does this equation embrace?

15.3 The specific latent heat of vaporisation of water is $2.25 \, \mathrm{MJ \, kg^{-1}}$. When $50 \, \mathrm{cm^3}$ of water (density $1000 \, \mathrm{kg \, m^{-3}}$) at $100\,°C$ is changed into steam at $100\,°C$ and a constant pressure of 101 kPa, $0.083 \, \mathrm{m^3}$ of steam is formed. Calculate: (a) the mass of $50 \, \mathrm{cm^3}$ of water, (b) the energy needed to produce this amount of steam, (c) the work done during the vaporisation and (d) the increase in the internal energy. (e) What happens to the internal energy absorbed during the process of vaporisation?

Chapter 16

16.1 Describe in words the changes of energy that occur when a trolley oscillates between springs on the bench. Eventually the trolley stops oscillating. Describe what has happened to the energy.

16.2 Describe the energy changes that occur when a mass oscillating on the end of a vertical spring moves from the lowest position through the middle to the

highest position of its motion. Assume that the spring remains under tension all the time.

16.3 A mass of 600 g is restrained by a spring system of constant $250 \, \mathrm{N \, m^{-1}}$. The mass is displaced 8 cm from the equilibrium position. Calculate the potential energy given to the system. State the kinetic energy of the system in the centre of its motion and calculate the speed of the mass. Use this speed to estimate the period of the motion. Compare this with the value calculated from $T = 2\pi\sqrt{(m/k)}$. Comment on the difference you find.

Chapter 17

17.1 List the main primary energy sources used throughout the world. Contrast the usage in Central Africa with that in the United Kingdom.

17.2 When a nucleus of uranium-238 absorbs a neutron, it undergoes radioactive decay rather than nuclear fission. Why is this a problem in the design of a nuclear reactor? What is the purpose of the moderator in a nuclear reactor? Explain how the output power from a reactor is controlled.

17.3 Describe how energy can be extracted from 'hot rocks' in the Earth's surface. One of the problems in setting up a geothermal power station is that depths of over 5 km are required to achieve sufficiently high temperatures. Describe two other possible problems associated with a geothermal power station.

Chapter 18

18.1 Hydroelectric power stations using natural lakes provide a *renewable resource* with a *finite lifetime*. Explain these two, possibly contradicting, terms in this statement.

18.2 Sketch the structure of a solar panel and describe how it uses the Sun's energy to provide heating.

18.3 What is meant by the *solar constant*? The Earth follows an elliptical orbit about the Sun. Why is the solar constant greater in December than it is in June?

Chapter 19

19.1 Explain what is meant by a *heat engine*. What steps would you take to make the efficiency of a heat engine as large as possible?

19.2 A thermocouple has two junctions at 400 °C and 27 °C respectively. Calculate its maximum possible efficiency.

19.3 The Sun's internal temperature is 5 000 000 K. The average temperature of the universe is about 3 K. Calculate the maximum efficiency of a heat engine operating between these temperatures.

Examination questions

1. How would you recognise whether or not a mercury-in-glass thermometer is in a state of thermal equilibrium? [1]

   What physical requirement must be satisfied for a mercury-in-glass thermometer to be in a state of thermal equilibrium with water in a beaker? [1]

   A scale graduated in centimetres is attached to a mercury-in-glass thermometer. The length of the mercury thread is 6.21 cm when the thermometer is placed in an equilibrium mixture of ice and water. Its length is 27.35 cm when the thermometer is immersed in steam. Calculate its length when the temperature is 63.9 °C. [3]

   State two advantages of thermocouple thermometers compared with mercury-in-glass thermometers. [2]

   A thermocouple has the cold junction immersed in an ice–water mix at 0 °C. When the hot junction is in boiling water, the e.m.f. is 1.65 mV. Estimate the temperature of the hot junction when the e.m.f. is 1.47 mV. [3]

2. The relationship pV = constant applies to a sample of gas provided that two other physical variables are constant. Name them. [2]

   With the aid of a diagram, describe carefully how you would test the relationship by experiment. [6]

   Explain what is meant by the term *critical temperature*. [1]

3. The diagram shows a submarine of total volume 200 m³ whose depth below the surface of the sea is controlled by the amount of sea water held in a storage tank. The submarine is cruising below the surface. The storage tank contains 10 m³ of sea water. The density of sea water is 1025 kg m⁻³.

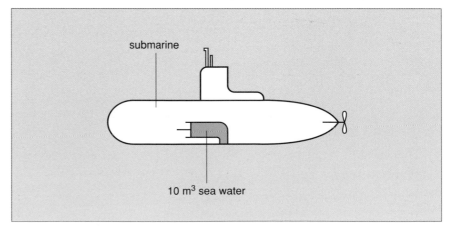

   Calculate the mass of the submarine and its contents. [2]

If the atmospheric pressure is 1.00×10^5 Pa, calculate the energy needed to empty the water storage tank when the water outlet is 25 m below the sea surface. [4]

The sea water has now been pumped out of the storage tank. Calculate the net upward force on the submarine. [2]

Calculate the maximum value for the upward acceleration of the submarine. [2]

4 A partially inflated balloon containing hydrogen carries meteorological equipment up through the atmosphere. Over a short distance its upward speed is almost constant. Copy, complete and label the diagram to show the forces acting on the balloon. [3]

Explain what can be deduced about the resultant force on the balloon. [2]

The balloon would not rise if the hydrogen were replaced by an identical volume of air at the same temperature and pressure. Explain why not. [2]

Explain what happens to each of the following as the balloon and equipment rise a significant distance through the atmosphere:
(a) the pressure of the hydrogen and (b) the volume of the hydrogen. [4]

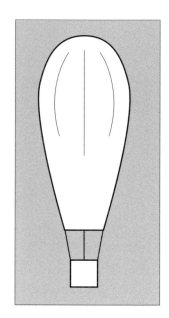

5 Two gas containers, A and B, have equal volumes and contain different gases at the same temperature and pressure. Use the ideal gas equation to show that there are equal numbers of molecules in the two containers. [3]

The molecules in container A have mass four times as great as the molecules in container B. Sketch and label graphs to show how the molecular speeds are distributed in the two containers, given that the speed distribution curve for the molecules in container A peaks at $200\,\text{m s}^{-1}$. [3]

How does kinetic theory account for the equal pressures at the same temperature and volume? [3]

6 The diagram illustrates high-pressure air expelling a disc from a cylinder.

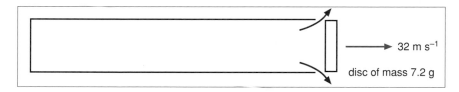

The mass of the disc is 7.2 g and its maximum speed is $32\,\text{m s}^{-1}$. Calculate the energy transferred to the disc. [3]

How would you use the kinetic theory of gases to account for the cooling of the air in the cylinder during the expulsion of the disc? [3]

Explain why work is done by the air on the disc but no work is done by the disc on the air. [2]

7   A mass is oscillating vertically on the end of a spring. Explain what happens to the following quantities as the mass rises from the bottom of its motion to the top: (a) kinetic energy, (b) gravitational potential energy and (c) elastic potential energy.   [4]

   After a long time, the mass stops oscillating. What has happened to the energy?   [2]

8   The period of a pendulum is 2.2 s. Its bob has a maximum speed of $0.46\,\mathrm{m\,s^{-1}}$ and a mass of 65 g. Calculate the maximum kinetic energy of the bob.   [1]

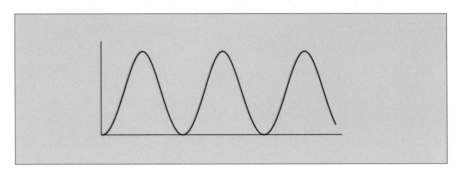

   The graph shows how the kinetic energy W of the pendulum bob varies with time t. Copy the graph. On your graph, mark the axes with appropriate scales.   [2]

   Sketch and label two more lines on your graph, one to represent the variation of potential energy with time and a second line to represent the total mechanical energy stored in the system.   [2]

9   A 24 W filament lamp has been switched on for some time. In this situation the first law of thermodynamics, represented by the equation $\Delta U = \Delta Q + \Delta W$, may be applied to the lamp. State and explain the value of each of the terms in the equation during a period of two seconds of the lamp's operation.   [6]

   Typically, filament lamps have an efficiency of only a few percent. Explain what this means and how it is consistent with the law of conservation of energy. [2]

10   You are asked to measure the specific heat capacity of aluminium using a cylindrical block of aluminium, which has been drilled out to accept an electrical heater. Draw a complete diagram of the apparatus you would use. [3]

   Describe how you would carry out the experiment and list the measurements you would take.   [5]

   Explain how you would calculate the specific heat capacity of aluminium from your measurements.   [3]

11   A student pours 500 g of water into an aluminium saucepan of mass 1.20 kg, heats it over a steady flame and records the temperature as it heats up. The temperatures are plotted on the graph shown.

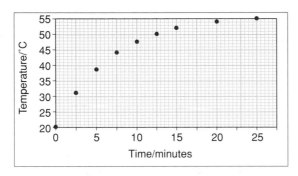

Calculate the total heat capacity of the saucepan and water. [Specific heat capacity of water = $4200 \, \text{J} \, \text{kg}^{-1} \text{K}^{-1}$ and specific heat capacity of aluminium = $900 \, \text{J} \, \text{kg}^{-1} \text{K}^{-1}$]   [3]

Find the rate of rise of water temperature at the beginning of the heating process.   [2]

Hence find the rate at which energy is supplied to the saucepan and water. [2]

Explain why the rate at which the temperature rises slows down progressively as the heating process continues.   [2]

12 What is a *biofuel*?   [1]

Give an example of a biofuel.   [1]

Why is it very inefficient to use biofuels to generate electricity for home heating rather than using them to heat homes directly?   [3]

13 The diagrams are of an evacuated heat-pipe solar collector. The heat-pipes contain a special fluid, which evaporates when heated and rises to the condensing unit. Here it condenses, thus warming the water, which flows through the heat exchanger. The fluid then falls back down the pipe and the cycle is repeated. These collectors are much more efficient than simple flat-plate collectors and supply hot water at significantly higher temperatures.

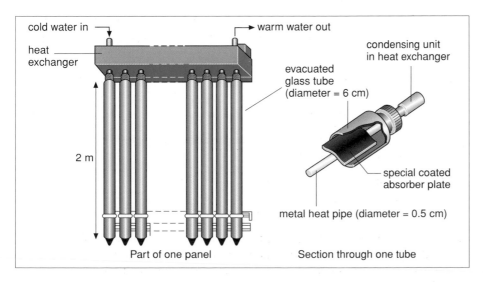

Identify two of the design features shown in the diagrams which account for the high efficiency. Explain in each case the physics principle employed.   [4]

Suppose that one of these collectors is 70% efficient. Estimate the area of collector required to produce hot water for an average household on a winter day. You may find the following data helpful:

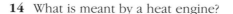

Solar flux at the collector's surface at midday on a fine day $= 0.9\,kW\,m^{-2}$
Specific heat capacity of water $= 4\,kJ\,kg^{-1}K^{-1}$
Average hot water consumption per household per day $= 80\,litres$
Mass of 1 litre of water $= 1\,kg$

State clearly any additional assumptions and approximations you make. [6]

14 What is meant by a heat engine? [3]

Explain why there is a constant search for materials to make turbine blades that will operate at higher temperatures to improve the efficiency of thermal power stations. [2]

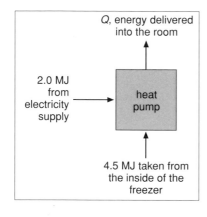

15 The working part of a freezer is a heat pump, which pumps energy from the inside of a freezer to the outside. The diagram shows the energy flows for one day of operation.

What is the value of Q, the energy flow out of the freezer? [1]

State the physical law you used to calculate your answer. [1]

Suggest a reason why you need an energy source to pump energy from the inside of the freezer to the outside. [1]

What is the power flow through the walls of the freezer? [1]

The freezer has an internal temperature of $-16\,°C$ and is in a room whose temperature is $20\,°C$. The walls of the freezer are made from insulating foam, 5 cm thick, and have an area of $4.1\,m^2$. Calculate the thermal conductivity of the insulating foam. [3]

Four containers of liquid milk, each having mass of 2.3 kg and initially at $0\,°C$, are placed in the freezer. It takes 24 hours before the milk freezes. [The specific latent heat of fusion of milk is $334\,kJ\,kg^{-1}$.] What is the extra energy that the heat pump must pump out of the freezer as the milk freezes? [3]

Inside the freezer there are no cooling fins at the bottom, but there are a large number of them towards the top. Explain how these fins cool the freezer and why there are none at the bottom. [2]

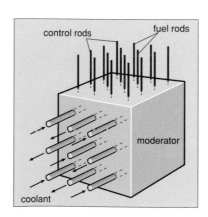

16 The diagram shows the essential components of a thermal fission reactor.

Explain the function of the moderator. [2]

Explain the function of the control rods. [2]

The energy released is transferred to the boiler of a turbine generator. Describe how energy is transferred from the fuel rods to the boiler. [4]

Electronics Topic

E1 Explain the term *output saturation* when applied to an operational amplifier. When does it occur? For an ideal operational amplifier, what are the values of: (a) the currents into both inputs of the op-amp, and (b) the voltage between the inputs if the output is not saturated?　　[4]

E2 The diagram shows a non-inverting amplifier. Explain the term non-inverting amplifier.　　[4]

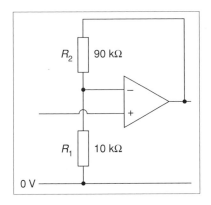

The closed-loop voltage gain of a non-inverting amplifier is given by the formula $1 + R_2/R_1$. Calculate the gain of the amplifier shown. Show how this expression for the closed-loop voltage gain is derived.　　[6]

E3 A non-inverting amplifier has power supply rails of $\pm 15\,\text{V}$. Give approximate maximum and minimum values for the output voltage. It is possible to use two light-emitting diodes with appropriate additional resistors to indicate whether the output of the op-amp is positive or negative. Draw a circuit to show how you would connect these to your non-inverting amplifier. The LEDs for this operation need a current of $3\,\text{mA}$ at a forward voltage of $2\,\text{V}$. Calculate values for the additional resistors required.　　[7]

E4 The diagram shows an op-amp used to make a nanoammeter to measure the ionisation current through an air gap. Copy the diagram and add a correctly connected dual-ended power supply.

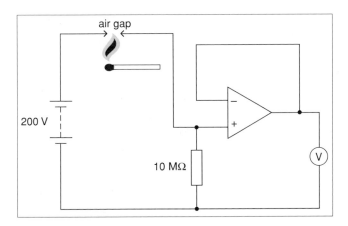

The ionisation current and the current through the voltmeter flow round two completely separate loops in the circuit you have drawn. Indicate, by labelling with P and Q respectively, the wires through which these current loops flow.　　[5]

E5 Op-amps can be used as comparators. Describe two differences in function between a comparator circuit and an amplifying circuit.　　[4]

E6 Draw a labelled circuit diagram of a simple amplitude-modulated radio receiver. Indicate on your diagram the parts which: (a) receive the frequency signal, (b) select the desired signal, (c) detect the signal and (d) smooth the signal.　　[6]

Medical Physics Topic

M1 Describe *photoelectric absorption* and *Compton scatter*. State and explain their relative importance in diagnosis and therapy. [6]

A 200 kV X-ray tube has a current of 150 mA. It produces an X-ray beam of diameter 1.5 mm. The efficiency of the tube is 0.6%. Calculate the intensity of the beam leaving the tube. State one assumption you have made in your calculation. [4]

M2 The graph shows the photon intensity–energy curve of a heterogeneous X-ray beam before and after passing through an aluminium filter of thickness 1.55 mm. Describe and explain the effect of filtration on: (a) the intensity of the X-ray beam and (b) the quality of the X-ray beam. [4]

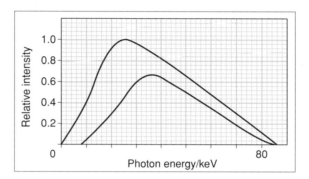

What mechanism is mainly responsible for the attenuation of the X-rays by the filter? For what photon energy is the half-value thickness in aluminium equal to 1.55 mm? Calculate the linear absorption coefficient in aluminium for X-rays of photon energy 35 keV. [6]

M3 Ultrasonic scanning depends upon the *sonar principle*. What is meant by the sonar principle? A patient has several pieces of glass embedded in his thigh, halfway up from the knee. Explain how an ultrasonic technique can be used to create an image of a cross-section of the leg to determine the positions of the larger pieces of glass. [8]

What factor determines the size of a piece of glass which is just too small to be detected? Explain your answer. If you were free to choose either ultrasonic or X-ray equipment for this task, which would you choose? Give reasons for your choice. [6]

M4 Thallium-208 is a beta-minus (β^-) emitter with a half-life of 3.1 minutes. It decays into an isotope of lead whose proton number is 82. Write an equation which describes its decay. [The symbol for thallium is Th and for lead is Pb.] Explain what problems might be encountered using this isotope of thallium for radio-nuclide imaging, assuming that there are no problems with its chemical behaviour. [4]

M5 Draw a diagram showing the essential components of a γ-camera. Your diagram should indicate the position of the patient and the origin of the γ-photons. Name a suitable isotope for use in this procedure. [7]

State three factors to be considered when choosing a radio-isotope suitable for use in diagnosis. [3]

M6 The nuclear magnetic resonance effect (NMR) is used for medical imaging. Images are produced from information collected from atoms in the body, particularly hydrogen atoms. In what sense is the technique *nuclear*? Explain the advantages of NMR over X-rays as an imaging method. NMR requires three separate magnetic fields. Explain the chief function of: (a) the strong uniform field, (b) the field gradient supplied by secondary coils and (c) the short pulse magnetic fields which oscillate at radio frequencies. [8]

Astrophysics Topic

A1 The activities which release energy within a main-sequence star such as the Sun cannot begin until the temperature near the star's centre approaches a value of 15 million K. Explain why this is so and how such a high temperature is produced. [4]

A2 List the steps in the p–p chain by which energy is released in stars such as the Sun. Explain why the process takes a long time to complete. [6]

Describe the physical processes which transport the energy released within the central core of a star such as the Sun to the surface of the star and away into space. [6]

A3 Two radiant sources of equal size have different Kelvin temperatures T_1 and T_2 where $T_1 = 2T_2$. Sketch two curves on a single graph comparing the radiant energy distributions against wavelength for the two radiant sources. Explain which features of your curves illustrate the Stefan–Boltzmann law and Wien's law. Explain which of these two laws you would expect to be of most help in estimating the temperature of a distant star. [8]

A4 Astronomers have discovered from their observations of the star Capella that (a) its surface temperature T is 5200 K, (b) its distance from the Earth is 4.3×10^{17} m and (c) at the Earth's surface the intensity of the radiation received from Capella is 1.2×10^{-8} W m^{-2}. Describe, in outline only, the parallax method for finding the distance of a star from the Earth. [4]

Calculate the radius r of Capella, given that its luminosity L can be found by using $L = 4\pi r^2 \sigma T^4$ where σ is the Stefan–Boltzmann constant which is 5.7×10^{-8} W m^{-2} K^{-4}. [3]

A5 Explain how the velocity of a star towards or away from the Earth can be found. [3]

A6 Show on a simple sketch of a Hertzsprung–Russell diagram, and in approximately the correct positions, a red giant star labelled R, a high-mass main-sequence star labelled M and a white dwarf star labelled W. With reference to their coordinates on your diagram, explain the physical significance of the descriptive titles *red giant* and *white dwarf*. [7]

Explain why main-sequence stars of large mass have higher luminosities and shorter lives than main-sequence stars of low mass. [5]

Describe the processes which occur within a star similar in mass to the Sun when it leaves the main sequence. [5]

It is thought that black holes are the end states of high-mass main-sequence stars. Explain how, in the right circumstances, it may be possible to detect the presence of a black hole. [3]

Things you need to know

Chapter 1

calibrate: to mark or adjust gradations on a scale by comparison with an accurate standard

ice point: the temperature (0°C) at which ice is at equilibrium with water in liquid form at a pressure of one atmosphere

boiling point: the temperature (100°C for pure water at atmospheric pressure) at which a liquid boils

thermal equilibrium: being at the same temperature

Chapter 2

macroscopic properties: large-scale gas properties that can be observed in the laboratory

isothermal: at constant temperature

Boyle's law: for a fixed mass of gas at constant temperature, the product of pressure and volume is constant

Chapter 3

absolute zero: the zero of the Kelvin scale of temperature (−273.15°C); the lowest temperature theoretically possible

pressure law: for a fixed mass of gas at constant volume, the pressure is directly proportional to the Kelvin temperature

critical temperature: a gas cannot be liquefied when above its critical temperature

ideal gas: a gas that obeys the **ideal gas equation** $pV = (m/M)RT$ in all situations – it does not liquefy

constant-volume gas thermometer: an instrument for measuring Kelvin temperature

molar mass: the mass of one mole of a substance

Chapter 4

pressure: force acting per unit area

Chapter 5

upthrust: upward force acting on an immersed object due to the difference in the fluid pressure acting on its top and its bottom

Archimedes' principle: when an object is, wholly or partially, immersed in a fluid it experiences an upthrust equal to the weight of fluid displaced

aerodynamic lift: force lifting aircraft caused by pressure on top of wing being less than that underneath

Chapter 6

terminal speed (terminal velocity): the maximum speed attained by an object falling through a fluid

drag: opposition of a fluid to the movement of an object through it

viscous force: frictional force that occurs between fluid layers moving at different speeds

Chapter 7

Brownian motion: the random motion of visible particles caused by random impacts from invisible molecules

Chapter 8

root mean square (r.m.s.) speed: the square root of the mean square speed, where the mean square speed is the sum of the squares of the molecular speeds divided by the total number of molecules

THINGS YOU NEED TO KNOW

Chapter 9

internal energy: random kinetic and potential energy of the molecules of a body

degrees of freedom: the number of independent ways, in which a molecule can move, spin or vibrate

heat or **heat transfer:** the energy transferred as a result of temperature difference

Chapter 10

thermal conduction: flow of internal energy through a material without the material itself moving

convection: thermal transmission of energy as a result of the material moving and taking energy with it

evaporation: process by which a substance changes into vapour at a temperature below its boiling point

steady state: where all temperatures throughout a material are remaining constant, producing a steady flow of internal energy

Chapter 11

thermal conductivity: the rate of flow of thermal energy through unit cross-sectional area of material in the presence of a unit temperature gradient

U-**value:** effective thermal conductivity per unit thickness for a given building construction

Chapter 12

heat capacity: energy needed to raise the temperature of that body by 1 K

specific heat capacity (or **specific enthalpy**): energy needed to raise the temperature of 1 kg of that substance by 1 K without a change of state

Chapter 13

specific latent heat of vaporisation (or **specific enthalpy of vaporisation**): energy needed to turn 1 kg of liquid into vapour at a constant temperature (its boiling point)

specific latent heat of fusion (or **specific enthalpy of fusion**): energy needed to turn 1 kg of solid into liquid at a constant temperature (its melting point)

Chapter 14

mechanical working: process in which energy transfer occurs when a force moves through a distance

electrical working: process when a voltage pushes charge through a distance

heating: process in which energy transfer is driven by a temperature difference, energy flowing from hot to cold

Chapter 15

first law of thermodynamics: increase in internal energy (ΔU) = energy transferred by heating (ΔQ) + energy transferred by working (ΔW)

Chapter 17

primary energy source: raw sources of energy

fossil fuel: coal, oil and gas produced in the Earth by a process of fossilisation

chain reaction: a process where the products (neutrons) of a reaction stimulate one or more further reactions

fuel rod: nuclear fuel in rod form for use in a reactor

moderator: material, such as graphite, used to slow down neutrons in a nuclear reactor

control rod: a boron rod moved in and out of a reactor core to vary the reactivity rate

finite resource: exhaustible energy source, which is being used up faster than it is being formed

Chapter 18

renewable resource: alternative energy source, such as hydroelectric, wind or solar power, that can be considered inexhaustible

biofuel: plant grown as an energy source

photovoltaic cell: a device for using sunlight to generate electricity directly

solar constant: power of Sun's rays falling normally on unit area at the top of the atmosphere

Chapter 19

heat engine: a device that takes energy from a hot source, uses some of this to do mechanical work, and gives the rest to a cold sink

Equations to learn

Ideal gas equation
$$pV = (m/M)RT$$
$$p_1V_1/T_1 = p_2V_2/T_2$$

Index

References to tables and illustrations are shown in italics if there is not already a text reference for that page.

INDEX